GRANNIES' REMEDIES

****

GRANNIES' REMEDIES

By MAI THOMAS

Gramercy Publishing Company • New York

A WORD OF CAUTION

Grannie was at best an enlightened amateur. Before actually using any of her remedies, you should consult your doctor.

This edition published by Gramercy Publishing Company
a division of Crown Publishers, Inc.,
by arrangement with James H. Heineman, Inc.

H

Library of Congress Catalogue Card No. 66–27823
© MCMLXV Wolfe Publishing Ltd.
British Publisher: Wolfe Publishing Ltd.

Contents

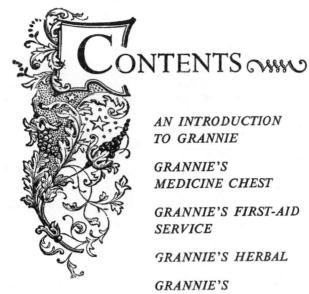

An Introduction to
Grannie

AROUND the turn of the century, when life was a great deal simpler, my grandmother lived in a grey stone cottage in a village on the borders of England and Wales.

It was a pleasant dwelling-place, which had stood in its overgrown garden of roses, hollyhocks, sweet peas, lavender, gooseberry bushes and gnarled old fruit trees since the days of the first Queen Elizabeth. The four small bedrooms had sloping floors, low ceilings, and little leaded windows that looked across lush pastures and a winding river to the blue Welsh hills. There was a kitchen with an enormous black-leaded range and a mass of shining copper pans, and a sink where the water came out of a hand-pump. And, heart and centre of all, there was the big, sunny sitting-room which seemed to the eyes of one small girl, at least, the most fascinating treasure-house on earth.

On the wall above the fireplace hung a bell-mouthed blunderbuss with which, so legend said, my grandfather had once driven off a highwayman. White china dogs stared glassily from either end of the chimney-piece, flanking a porcelain mandarin whose head nodded entrancingly at the gentlest touch. On the window-ledge, between the old-fashioned potted plants, there were great spiky sea shells brought in some clipper ship from the South Seas. When you put them to your ear, you could distinctly hear the roaring of the waves. There was a glass-fronted cabinet filled with Dresden shepherdesses, eggshell coffee cups, ivory Buddhas and elephants, and a globe which, when shaken, produced a most satisfactory snowstorm around a miniature pagoda.

This was the domain of my grandmother, a stately old lady dressed invariably in a black silk gown, with a shawl about her shoulders and a scrupulously laundered white lace cap atop her grey hair.

She was a small, slim woman, very graceful and un-ashamedly proud of her small hands and feet. Her dark eyes and warmly brown skin, coupled with the high cheekbones, betrayed the strain of Romany in her blood. Except for a touch of rheumatism in her hands, she was perfectly fit and active and would accept no help either with the housework or with the gardening.

She lived alone. Her husband, my grandfather, had been lost with his ship many years before I was born. She had reared her children and seen them settled in their own homes. Now, perfectly content and fiercely independent, she busied herself with the life of the village and the surrounding farms.

When she went out, if the weather were not too inclement, she wore what I believe was called a dolman and a perky little bonnet with an osprey plume and broad purple ribbons tied beneath her chin. In winter, she affected a close-fitting, red-squirrel jacket with a kind of mutton-chop sleeve and red woollen mittens. Almost invariably she carried a long, slim umbrella, the handle fashioned like a bird's head, but I never saw her open it, even when the rain was teeming down.

The villagers held her in almost awed respect. Some even whispered that she was a "white" witch. Whatever the truth of that claim (and she never troubled to deny it), certain it is that as soon as crisis hit the village—whether childbirth, death, measles, mumps, or some ailment among the livestock—within minutes somebody would be knocking on her back door.

She had, of course, no medical training in the accepted sense, yet for miles around people had very much more faith in her treatment than in the conventional skill of the local doctor with his top hat, wooden stethoscope and mysterious little black bag. Grannie's remedies *worked*, they said.

*　　　*　　　*

The origin of those remedies, which my grandmother had been collecting throughout her long life, is obscure. Some undoubtedly were handed down from her Romany forebears; others might well have had an ancestry dating back to the Druids. Some were so spartan, even terrifying, that the very thought of undergoing treatment might have produced an instantaneous "cure."

To cure whooping cough, my grandmother said, some people recommended that you skin a mouse, roast it, and give it to the sufferer to eat. If the patient were "finnicky," they suggested the treatment be disguised by baking the mouse in a patty.

Fortunately, Grannie didn't favour this remedy, but she told me that a common method of getting rid of tapeworm was to make the patient fast for three or four days. Then, in the same room, a large steak would be cooked and held in front of the patient's mouth, whereupon the ravenous tapeworm would shoot out of the patient's mouth, eager to get at the meat!

Less drastic was her treatment for ague. First, she said, you must cut an apple into three parts, on which you must write *Deus Pater*, *Deus Filius*, and *Deus Sanctus Spiritus*. The patient must fast for three days. At midnight on the first day, he must eat the section inscribed *Deus Pater*, and at midnight on the second day, the piece marked *Deus Filius*. At midnight on the third day, he ate the remaining portion, and the fever would leave him immediately.

Foolish? Well, the basic management for some fevers today is a starvation diet—which was just what my grandmother ordered. And no doubt the "mystic" words helped the cure along.

In this atomic age, thousands of people believe firmly that whooping cough can be cured by taking the sufferer for a trip in an aeroplane. Is that more credible than Grannie's mouse patty story?

My grandmother died quietly and without fuss at the age of 95. After her death I found in the old cottage a collection of school exercise books, each filled with her careful copper-plate handwriting. Through the years she had patiently compiled a pharmacopeia of folk-medicine for the guidance of those who should come after her.

This book is a selection of Grannie's remedies. It is also a memorial to a very good and great old lady, whose like we shall never see again.

I

Grannie's Medicine Chest

RANNIE'S "dispensary" was a large Georgian mahogany press, which stood in its own alcove in the sitting-room. Its contents might not have won a vote of confidence from any Medical Association, but they were undoubtedly comprehensive.

These, according to a list in her own firm handwriting, were the medicines and appurtenances essential in every home:

Three thermometers
Condy's Fluid and carbolic fluid
Lint, old rags, and gutta-percha
    tissue
Carron oil
Linseed meal
Flour of mustard
Rigollet's mustard leaves
Flannel for compresses
Bandages
A spatula
Castor oil
Quinine

Chlorodyne
Carbolic smoke ball
Sal volatile
Camphorated spirits
Hazeline
Ammonia
Diachylon
An india-rubber hot-water
    bottle
An enema
Elliman's Embrocation
Syringes
A feeding cup

| Medicine glasses with | Cotton wool |
| measurement | Arnica liniment |

At the bottom of the list was this note:

Medicine Stains

"Medicine stains may be removed from silver spoons by rubbing them with a rag dipped in dilute sulphuric acid and washing it off with soapsuds."

Domestic Measures

Domestic measures can be approximately gauged this way:

A wine-glassful (ordinary size)	= 1 fluid oz. and a half
Two tablespoonsful	= 1 fluid oz.
One tablespoonful	= half-fluid oz.
One dessertspoonful	= two drachms
One teaspoonful	= one drachm

These measurements apply solely to fluids—never to solids. A tablespoonful of some solids, as powders, would weigh two or three ounces, some granules one ounce.

Somewhat ahead of her time in this respect at least, Grannie firmly believed in dealing with germs before they had time to get into the human system, as the following notes show:

Disinfectant

Dissolve together in a gallon of water 4 oz. of zinc sulphate and 2 oz. of common salt.

Disinfectants for Rooms

To disinfect a room, etc. close the room windows and doors and chimneys to exclude outer air. Break roll sulphur in small pieces; place on a metal dish, and set this on a pair of tongs over a metal pot in which there is water, or over a large box of sand, to avoid danger of fire. Light it with a few hot coals or methylated spirit poured around the sulphur. Leave the room and shut the door. A pound and a half of sulphur is sufficient for 1,000 cubic feet of space. Keep the room closed three hours after the burning has ceased, then air well for six hours. Clothing and bedding may be hung on lines and left in the room.

Similarly, she was convinced that flies, bugs and such "varmints" had much to do with the spread of sickness, and had her own drastic methods of dealing with them:

To make an Ant Trap

Soak a sponge in water and wring it near-dry. Sprinkle with sugar and lay on a plate by the ants' haunts. As soon as it is full, plunge it into boiling water.

Ants, to Exterminate in Gardens

Mix a tablespoonful of carbolic acid with a basin of water and apply to nests. In the house, place cayenne where they are most seen, and scrub shelves, etc., with carbolic soap.

Another way is to boil 1 lb. of Cape aloes in a gallon of water and add 6 oz. of powdered camphor. Excavate an ant-hill, pour a quart of this into it, and cover as much area as possible, then fill the excavation. When the nest cannot be found, mix this *largely* with water and sprinkle on the leaves, etc., through the rose of a watering can.

Crickets

Put cucumber peel on the floor at night near their hiding-places. This will destroy them. It also destroys beetles.

Emetic Mixture

(For children): The safest emetic is ipecacuanha wine.

Give doses of half a teaspoonful to a teaspoonful in sweetened water, followed by draughts of tepid water. Repeat every 10 minutes till vomiting results.

(For adults): 1—Take 1 to 2 teaspoonsful powdered mustard. Mix in a tumblerful of warm water.

2—Take 20 grains of sulphate of zinc and a tumblerful of water. Mix, and give as an emetic, to be followed by long draughts of tepid water. This is good in cases of drug poisoning.

Emulsion of Gum Arabic

Take 2 drachms gum arabic powder, sweet almonds, blanched, white sugar, half an ounce of each. Warm a pint of barley water, dissolve the gum in it, and when almost cold, pour slowly on the almonds, which should have been previously beaten to powder with the sugar to form a milky mixture, then strained. This is useful for common colds.

Epsom Salts

Adult dose is half an ounce, taken first thing in the morning with a warm drink afterwards. An excellent saline purgative.

Flies

The best remedy for getting rid of flies is Myocom or fly-gum. Also a piece of flannel saturated with turpentine put on a plate will get rid of the flies. Pyrethrum or Persian insect powder will free a room of flies if blown about with a small bellows. Wood ashes thrown into drains and on rubbish heaps destroys the flies' eggs. A ⅞ oz. of quassia chips boiled in a pint of water and mixed with 4 oz. of treacle draws flies and kills them. Fried camomile flowers scattered about gets rid of fleas. They can't tolerate the smell.

To protect yourself from flies and gnats, sponge weak carbolic acid on the skin, and sometimes, clothing. The solution should not contain more than 7 per cent carbolic acid.

Mustard

If you've got some English mustard handy, you have always got an efficient emetic. A full teaspoonful in a tumblerful of warm water generally produces vomiting. If it doesn't act within 10 minutes, it can be repeated. If still ineffective, a third dose can be given in another 10 minutes.

It is particularly useful for drunkenness, narcotic, and other poisoning, as well as in all cases where the stomach is overloaded with indigestible food and it is necessary to empty the stomach without depressing the system.

Mustard Poultices

Usually made with the flour of mustard mixed to the consistence of a poultice with water or vinegar, spread on a piece of thick brown paper or rag, and apply to the skin. Cold water should be used in their preparation. It is wrong to use, as some do, hot water or vinegar.

For anyone with a delicate skin it is advisable to place a piece of thin muslin between the poultice and skin. Always remove if it produces redness, whether it causes pain or not. A poultice should be instantly removed if it causes severe pain, otherwise it is liable to blister the skin and cause difficult-to-heal ulcers.

Some mustard poultices are made of a combination of one part mustard and four parts linseed meal. Mix the mustard with warm water in a separate vessel. Mix linseed meal with boiling water, add the mustard mixture, and stir with the meal. Spread on linen, and apply for 3 or 4 hours.

Poultices are seldom used nowadays because they are heavy, messy, and generally inferior to fomentations. Never use them for infants with chest affections, as they affect the breathing.

Linseed Poultice

Pour boiling water into a previously warmed basin and sprinkle in the meal, stirring constantly with a broad-bladed knife, until thick paste is formed. Spread the paste on a piece of linen or a layer of tow, and turn in the edges all round. A piece of fine muslin dipped in olive oil can be laid on the paste to prevent it sticking to the skin. Secure it to the affected part with bandage. Change every 3 or 4 hours.

Bran Poultices

Are lighter than linseed, and can be used several times. Make a flannel bag to the size required and fill with bran. Wrap loosely in a towel, pour boiling water over it, and wring out as with a fomentation.

Another good and very simple poultice is a piece of soft thick sheet-lint, doubled, squeezed out in hot water, and laid over the part, covered with a larger piece of thin rubber-sheeting.

Bread Poultice

Put half a pint of boiling water over a sufficient quantity of bread-crumbs; stir until a soft mass; spread a half-an-inch thick over a large cloth, and apply.

Yeast Poultice

Made by mixing a pound of flour or linseed meal with half-a-pint of yeast. The mixture should be heated and carefully stirred.

Charcoal Poultice

For charcoal poultice soak 2 oz. of bread-crumbs for 10 minutes in ½ pint of boiling water, then mix. Gradually add half-an-ounce of powdered wood charcoal, and 1½ oz. of linseed meal. The whole should be well stirred, and spread and applied in the ordinary way.

Insects and Vermin

Dissolve 2 lbs. of alum in 3 quarts of water. Wait until the alum is dissolved, then with a brush apply boiling hot to every joint and crevice infested by bugs, earwigs, or other insects. Keep it boiling whilst using. Strong boiling hot tea of cayenne used with a brush is also a good remedy.

Leather (to Vermin-proof)

Castor oil mixed with tallow will vermin-proof leather.

Lint

Can be quickly made by nailing a piece of old linen on a board, and scraping its surface with a knife. Scraped lint is the fine filaments from ordinary lint, and is used to stimulate ulcers and absorb discharges.

Moths

Anything moth-infested should be damped with benzine. It harms nothing but the moth.

A brick kept damp, and raised one-eighth of an inch from the floor, will collect moths under it. Once weekly, raise the brick and crush the moths or, take a small bunch of red wool, place on a piece of paper on the floor of a cupboard, and the moths will collect. Every few days, if the wool is shaken, moths will drop on the paper and can be destroyed. When clothes are infested, take a large linen cloth and wet thoroughly. Lay it folded two or three times over the affected part, and press with a very hot iron. This will destroy the larvae and eggs.

Moths in feathers can be destroyed by making openings in the bed-pillow, or whatever article they may be in, and placing lumps of camphor among them, or by putting the feathers in sacks, washing them, and drying well for days in sunlight.

Moths like the turnings and corners of carpets. Wring a cloth out of hot water, lay over the bindings and edgings, and iron with a very hot iron. Hold the iron on until the cloth is dry.

Another way is to wipe floors with a cloth wrung out of strong, hot cayenne tea, leaving the carpet turned back long enough for the floor to dry before replacing, wring a clean cloth dry out of this hot pepper tea, and wipe the binding and carpet edge rubbing hard. Salt sprinkled on pieces of cotton wool dipped in turpentine, put under the carpet edges can also be successful.

Finally, for a good moth preventative, mix 12 drops of oil of cloves, 12 drops of caraway, 6 drops of oil of lavender, a glass of whisky, and a piece of camphor. Sprinkle with it. Cedar-wood shavings are also death to moths.

Slugs

Put cabbage leaves in an oven till soft; rub with fresh dripping and lay wherever the slugs are. The leaves will soon be found covered with slugs and snails.

Smell of Paint

Paint smell can be removed by shutting the room; placing in the middle of it a pan of lighted charcoal on which some juniper berries have been thrown.

A handful of hay in a pail of water is another effective method.

From health contentment springs . . .

The best physicians are Dr. Diet, Dr. Quiet, and Mr. Merryman

A handful of good life is better than a bushel of good learning

He that would have a clear head, must have a clean stomach

By examining the tongue of a patient physicians find out the diseases of the body, and philosophers the diseases of mind

*Reason's whole pleasure, all the Joys of Sense
Lie in three words, Health, Peace and Competence
But Health consists in temperance alone
And Peace, oh Virtue! Peace is all thy own*

You should not touch your eye but with your elbow

The man who spends his energies deliberately, has the most inexhaustible bank to draw upon, and will draw the longest

19

2

Grannie's First-Aid Service

IFE in a country village can be fuller and more hazardous than the city dweller would suspect, and hardly a day passed without Grannie being called out in a hurry. Her accident cases were varied and colourful, as the following "stock" remedies show:

Antidote

For alcohol, opium, prussic acid, strychnine and all poisoning.

Take a heaped teaspoonful each of common salt and ground mustard stirred quickly in a glass of warm water, and swallow immediately. This causes instant vomiting. When vomiting stops, swallow the whites of two eggs, then drink plenty of strong coffee.

Bleeding

To stop bleeding, use powdered rice sprinkled on lint and

applied to the wound, or put a handful of flour over the cut. If there is a cobweb handy, bind it on the wound and bleeding will stop. An application of Hazeline also stops it.

Bruises

Rest and bathe in cold water. If skin is unbroken, apply half-a-teaspoonful of arnica lotion to a tumbler of water. Wet soft linen rags with this lotion, and apply and change

as often as they dry. Alternatively, wring out a cloth in hot water and lay on the affected part. Renew frequently till pain eases.

Bruises of the Finger

The fastest way of getting relief after the occurrence of the accident is to plunge the finger into water as hot as can be borne. By so doing, the nail is softened and allows the blood to pour out beneath it, thereby soon relieving the pain. The finger may then be wrapped in a bread and water poultice.

For bruises, sprains, contusions, and local inflammations, diluted vinegar is also a popular and useful application.

Or, you can immediately apply treacle spread on brown paper. Or a plaster of chopped parsley mixed with butter.

To prevent a bruise swelling, instantly apply a cloth, 5 or 6 times doubled, dipped in cold water, and re-dip when it gets too dry and warm.

To cure a bruise swelling, foment it half-an-hour, morning and night, with cloths dipped in water as hot as you can bear.

Burns (slight)

Immediately apply pulverised charcoal and linseed oil. Common soda moistened with water applied quickly is effective. Freely use soft soap, then linseed oil and sift over the burn, wheaten flour. When this dries hard, repeat the oil and flour till a complete covering is obtained. Let this dry till it falls off and a new skin forms.

[*Important: Ideas on the treatment of burns have changed radically since Grannie's days. You are now strongly advised that the only dressing you should apply is a dry clean piece of linen—and to get the doctor's advice immediately. You should not remove clothes unless it is impossible to reach a hospital or doctor.*]

To dress a burn, mix equal parts of linseed oil and lime water, saturate a cloth with it, and bind on the burn. This is the carron oil used by surgeons.

Instantly, in the case of scald or burn, cover the injury with a sheet, or a portion of sheet, or wadding, taking care not to break any blister that may have formed.

Envelop every part of the injury from all access of the air, laying one or two more pieces of wadding on first to effectually guard the burn or scald from atmospheric irritation.

A light bandage should finally secure the dressings in place. Exclusion of air from a burn or scald is the best, quickest, and least painful treatment.

To treat burns, take chalk and linseed, or common olive oil, and mix into a compound as thick as honey.

Add vinegar to reduce the thickness if necessary. Apply with a soft brush and renew the application from time to time.

Choking from Fish Bone

When a person has a fish bone in the throat, insert the forefinger, press upon the root of the tongue, so as to induce vomiting; if this does not do, let him swallow a large piece of potato or soft bread; and if these fail, give a mustard emetic.

Convulsions

Throw cold water on the face and sponge the head with it. Put the child into a hot bath of mustard and water (100° F). Keep the child in the bath 15 minutes or until better. Rub thoroughly dry and wrap warmly. Your doctor should be summoned immediately and his advice taken.

Dog Bites

If there is doubt about the dog, suck the wound and plunge a lighted vesuvian into the wound. For ordinary dog-bites, spread a thick paste of carbonate of soda and water over the wound and bind. Lance the surface around the wound and let it bleed freely in tepid water, to which pink Condy has been added.

Rabies

If bitten, take immediately 1½ oz. of the root of the ele-campane plant (the green root is preferable). Slice or bruise it, put into a pint of fresh milk, boil down to half-a-pint, strain, and drink when cold. Fast at least 6 hours afterwards. Next morning repeat the dose and fast, using

2 oz. of the root. On the third morning take a third dose. Remember, eat nothing for 6 hours after each dose.

A man was said to have been cured of hydrophobia by being put in a cellar alone with nothing to drink but brine left in a meat-barrel. After having several fits his thirst was so intense that he drank the brine. He had no more fits. It is impossible to check the truth of this story.

Mad Animals (Bites)

Tie string tightly over the part, cut out the bite and cauterise the wound with carbolic fluid. Then apply a piece of spongio-piline; give a purgative and plenty of warm drink.

Ears

To remove insects from the ear, gently use a warm-water syringe. But this is a job for a doctor or nurse.

Eyes

To remove substances from the eyes, bathe with luke-warm water till clear. If stubborn, raise the lid gently and pass a soft camel-hair brush along it.

When dust gets into the eyes, dash cold water into them. If this doesn't do the trick, you can either syringe the eye with lukewarm water or, placing your forefinger upon the cheek-bone, slightly bend the finger to draw down the lower lid, and you will probably be able to remove the dirt. If not, repeat the operation with a cleaned matchstick over the upper lid; ask the patient to look down, then turn the lid upwards over the needle. This will turn it inside out, and should enable you to remove the trouble with the corner of a handkerchief. As soon as the substance is removed, bathe the eye with cold water, drop in a drop of castor oil, and, if very sore, exclude the light for a few hours.

For inflamed eyes use the white of an egg beaten to a

froth and add 2 tablespoonsful of rosewater. Apply on a soft rag and change as often as it dries.

Face-ache

Apply with a flannel a mixture of 2 drs. ether, 2 drs. laudanum, 2 drs. camphorated spirits of wine, 2 oz. of sal-volatile. For external use only: laudanum is dangerous.

Faintness

Take 1 or 2 teaspoonsful of compound tincture of lavender whenever symptoms appear.

Fainting is due to failure of the heart's action, and can be caused by emotion; by breathing heated impure air; by loss of blood and other causes of shock; by diseases of the heart and digestive organs.

Treatment: Place the patient flat on his back, and loosen clothing. Give him fresh air by opening windows and making bystanders refrain from crowding round. Rub limbs briskly in an upward direction. If able to swallow, diluted brandy, sal volatile, or Eau de Cologne may be given by the mouth. If the attack shows signs of long duration, apply a mustard plaster or poultice over the heart. When recovery has taken place, do not allow him to attempt to stand for some time after he is conscious.

*   *   *

For faintness and prostration, take the whites and yolks of 3 eggs and beat them up in 5 oz. of plain water; add slowly 3 oz. of brandy with a little sugar of nutmeg. If the stomach is very irritable, take a tablespoonful of cream and beat it up thoroughly with the white of a new-laid egg. Add slowly to the frothy mixture one tablespoonful of brandy in which a lump of sugar has been dissolved.

Fits

These can be either epileptic or apoplectic. In the former, the unhappy person afflicted gives a scream, becomes deathly pale, falls on the face, becomes convulsed, then insensible.

Clothes should be loosened and a doctor summoned. In apoplectic fits, the person falls, goes purple in the face, and breathes in a snoring manner. Raise the head, apply cold water to it, and call a doctor.

Flea-bites

Rub the bites with Thilum, which is an Indian remedy.

Hiccough

Put some drops of vinegar on a piece of loaf sugar and eat slowly. Or, moisten brown sugar with vinegar and take a few grains to a teaspoonful. The effect is almost instantaneous.

Hysterics

Put the hysterical person on a bed, loosen clothing; slap the chest and face smartly with the end of a towel dipped in cold water. Don't be hard in your manner. Open-air exercise, strengthening diet, cheerful surroundings, with the removal of all care and perplexities is important as well as proper regularity of the bowels. Iron pills help. Strong tansy tea, taken cold and in small quantities, is good.

A long, narrow strip of strengthening-plaster, worn the entire length of the spine during cold weather, is also good. This may be made by mixing by heat, dark resin with half its proportion of beeswax, adding a few drops of olive oil.

Itching

Use a cone of cacao butter impregnated with 2 per cent cocaine. This should be rubbed over the affected part. The warm skin melts a layer of the cacao butter, to form a soothing emollient shield. This is good for irritating affections of the skin, and for insect bites.

Itch or scabies is due to a parasite which causes intense itching which is aggravated when the body becomes warm, as on first going to bed. Rub soft soap all over the body, and then take a hot bath and scrub with a nail-brush. Dry the skin, and then rub in sulphur ointment, which must not be washed off for 12 hours. Clothes must be baked.

To soothe the itching skin, a weak carbolic acid lotion, two grains to the ounce, diluted vinegar or alcohol, bicarbonate of soda solution, a teaspoonful or so to the pint.

Mosquito Stings

Apply a mixture of 50 grs. of powdered alum, 10 grs. or aromatic vinegar, 10 grs. of glycerine immediately. It soothes itching and pain.

Nettle Rash

Rub the parts with parsley.

Nettle-rash – Hives

Local remedies are important. They are conveniently applied in the form of lotions or baths; among the former are vinegar and water and alcohol and water. Bay rum may be used, soda, a drachm to half a pint of water, and weak solutions of carbolic acid.

Nettle Sting

Rub the part with juice of nettles.

Nose Bleed

Small pieces of ice may be sucked and inserted into the nostril, and a piece held against the side of the nose and forehead.

Or, firmly grasp the nose with the finger and thumb of the right hand for fully 10 or 15 minutes, thus completely stopping the movement of air through the nose.

Bleeding from the nose sometimes yields to a piece of rag saturated with vinegar introduced into the nostril. This may also generally be stopped by putting a plug of lint into the nostrils. If not, apply a cold lotion to the forehead, raise the head, and place over it both arms, so that it will rest on the hands; dip the lint plug in friar's balsam, or tincture of kino. Heat should be applied to the feet; and, in obstinate cases, the sudden shock of a cold key or cold water poured down the spine, will often instantly stop the bleeding. If the bowels are restricted, take a purgative.

* * *

Hot Packs

Are valuable in cases where it is necessary to sweat. The bed should be protected with a mackintosh, and a blanket laid over it. The patient should be stripped, and a blanket dipped in hot water and wrung out as dry as possible, thrown over him, with plenty of blankets overall.

Warm milk or barley-water will promote perspiration. After an interval of about half-an-hour, remove the wet blanket and rapidly swathe the patient in hot, dry blankets.

Wrapping a patient in hot blankets, giving him warm drinks, and the placing of hot-water bottles or heated bricks, well wrapped to prevent burning, in the bed is another means of promoting perspiration.

GRANNIES' REMEDIES

Dislocated Thumb

Frequently produced by a fall. Make a clove hitch by passing two loops of cord over the thumb, placing a piece of rag under the cord to prevent it cutting the thumb. Pull in the same line as the thumb. Apply a cold lotion, one part spirit to 3 parts water.

Dry Heat

Wool may be heated against a can containing boiling water and laid on affected parts. This is a useful way of applying heat in inflammations of the eye and joints. Heating wool in front of a fire is dangerous. A layer of dry, hot wool wrapped round a joint and covered with oiled-silk, rapidly becomes saturated with perspiration, and gives great relief in acute inflammation, such as gout and rheumatism. Change the wool frequently.

Noses

If a foreign substance gets up a child's nose, open the child's mouth, place your mouth over it, and blow gently to expel the substance. But better to get a doctor.

Poisons and Antidotes

Use the following treatments if no doctor is at hand:
Oil of Vitriol-Aquafortis-Muriatic Acid—Magnesia, chalk, soap and water every two minutes.
Tartar Emetic—Oily drinks and warm water.
Prussic Acid—Pump water on back, put strong-smelling salts to nose.
Arsenic—Emetics of mustard and salt, some water and sweet oil or milk.
Mercury-Corrosive Sublimate—Whites of eggs and milk in large quantities.
Opium-Laudanum—Strong coffee, emetic draught, vinegar and water, dash cold water on the face, walk up and down for 2 or 3 hours.

Lead—Castor oil and emetics, plus whites of eggs.

Verdigris—Whites of eggs, gruel, castor oil.

Henbane-Hemlock-Nightshade—Emetics and castor oil, brandy and
water.

Poisonous food—Emetics and castor oil.

Carbolic Acid—Flour and water and glutinous drinks.

Chloral Hydrate-Chloroform—Pour cold water over head and face.

Strychnine—Emetic of mustard and warm water.

Oxalic Acid—Magnesia dissolved in water every 2 minutes.

Snake-bites

Snake venom produces symptoms of shock, nausea, and
faintness, often accompanied by vomiting, followed by
intense lethargy, lapsing into coma. The bite of the English
viper is rarely fatal.

Treatment: Immediately tie a ligature tightly above
the wound, then suck the wound. This may be safely done
provided there are no cracks or sores on the mouth or lips.
Encourage bleeding. Wash the wound as soon as possible
with strong ammonia (such as sal volatile), Condy's fluid,
or tincture of iodine. The shock should be treated by
giving large doses of stimulants, preferably sal volatile,
and the patient must somehow be kept awake and from
yielding to lethargy.

In the tropics, the following drastic treatment is sometimes adopted: Tissues around the bites are pinched up
and cut away; a paste is then made of gunpowder and
blood and the wounds filled with it. The paste is then
ignited and the tissues consequently cauterised.

Sore Throat

An effective remedy for sore throat, especially when accompanied by hoarseness—onions boiled in molasses.

In relaxed, ulcerated, and other forms of sore throat
benefit is often derived by inhaling the vapour of hot
vinegar.

Sores and Cuts

Bathe with one part whisky and 3 parts water.

Sore or blistered heels should be prevented by wearing well-made boots for rough work, and by keeping the leather pliant with dubbin, tallow, or castor oil. Socks should be changed after a day's work, feet washed, and the skin hardened with surgical spirit. Strong salt and water may be used. Before starting in the morning, the feet should be greased with lanoline, petrol jelly, castor oil, tallow or mutton-fat.

If chafing or blistering occurs, the condition must be treated as in bed sores. The blister can be pricked, but the skin must not be removed. Blisters from rowing can be similarly prevented and treated.

Sprains

The injured member should be elevated and cold applications made to the joint either with cloths wrung out in cold water, or by powdered ice in towels or in a rubber bag. The best way of keeping cloths wet without changing them is to fill a jug with water, place it higher than the limb; moisten a strip of linen, place one end of it in the water, and let the other end hang on the outside. Rest it on the cloths that cover the injured place so that the water is continuously conducted to the linen.

As the sprain improves, it will require gentle rubbing with liniment.

Sunburn

Wash the face with sage-tea.

Sunstroke

Often affects people through severe muscular exertion in

hot sun. An attack is frequently sudden. The victim falls insensible, but usually there is headache, dizziness, and gradual loss of consciousness. The face flushes, the pulse is rapid, and temperature high.

Treatment: Loosen clothing and immediately pour cold water over the patient. Strip clothing, and if you have any ice, rub the body with it, otherwise cover the patient with a sheet and keep it drenched with cold water. As

consciousness returns, lots of cold water drinks should be given.

If still insensible, apply mustard-leaves to the nape of the neck, arms, and leg calves. After recovery, the patient is very sensitive to heat and should refrain from exposure to hot sun or exertion in hot weather for some time.

Stings and Bites

Bees, wasps and hornets: Extract the sting, if left in the flesh, and apply ammonia or bicarbonate of soda. You can also apply honey to a bee sting.

Gnats, mosquitos and ants: Ammonia or bicarbonate of soda.

Scorpions, centipedes, tropical spiders: Place a ligature above the wound, encourage bleeding, and apply ammonia, vinegar, or turpentine, followed by hot fomentations. Give stimulants if there are symptoms of shock.

Bee stings are best treated after the removal of the sting itself (which should be squeezed out by firm pressure of the thumb-nail), first by cooling, then by hot compresses. Covering the swelling with damp, cold earth is a good cure.

Jelly fish

Sea-bathers stung by them suffer nausea and faintness, as well as pain in the affected limb. A warm bath and a teaspoonful of sal volatile in water should be administered if there are signs of shock. On the sting itself, use bicarbonate of soda or ammonia.

An excellent lotion for such cases can be made with equal parts vinegar, arrack, and water. This is also good applied to the head for headache and fever delirium. The pains of venomous bites or stings is often speedily relieved by constant application of a piece of vinegar-moistened rag.

Weevers and Rays

Inflict troublesome wounds with their sharp spines. Suck the wound to promote bleeding, then wash the wound with Condy's fluid, ammonia, or bicarbonate of soda, and dress with olive oil.

Teething

Dill water is frequently administered to children during teething, when they appear to be griped by wind in the stomach and bowels. Attack the cause, as wind is usually the result of something more serious. Some magnesia can be given with the dill water, which should be used in doses of a teaspoonful or more to a year-old child.

Warts

Rub them daily with radish, or with juice of marigold flowers. It seldom fails. Or, rub the wart on a piece of raw meat.

Small doses of sulphate of magnesia taken internally can also remove warts. Three grains of Epsom salts taken morning and evening is a known cure in France. Apply twice or thrice daily some aromatic vinegar, dab on the skin with a fine camel-hair brush, taking care not to touch the surrounding skin, when most probably the wart will shrivel away.

A good ointment for warts, which should be applied daily, is made from a mixture made of 2 drs. muriate of ammonia, 1 oz. powdered savin, and 1½ oz. of lard.

Wounds

Before dressing a wound examine the colour of the blood. If it flows regularly and is dark, it can be dressed. If it is bright scarlet and spurts out in jets, put on a tourniquet and wash the part well with cold water, bring the edges of the wound together, and keep them together with strips of sticking plaster. Place some lint wet with friars' balsam on the cut, and secure with a bandage. Remember a tourniquet should never be left on too long at a time. A doctor must be consulted in the case of arterial bleeding and a note made of the time when the tourniquet was applied.

Where the wound is the plaster must be . . .

Music helps not the toothache

*Nor love they life nor hate: but what thou livest
Live well: how long or short, permit to heaven*

*The grand secret seems to be, to contrive that the
exercise of the body and that of the mind may serve
as relaxations to each other*

*Those who are candidates for health, must be as
circumspect in the task they set their mind as in the
exercise they give to their body*

*The patient can oftener do without the doctor than the
doctor without the patient*

*What we have been longest used to is most likely to
agree with us best*

Who steals an old man's supper does him no wrong

3

Grannie's
Herbal

HE BASIS of Grannie's healing powers was—
apart from a shrewd if untutored use of practical
psychology—an encyclopaedic knowledge of the
curative use of herbs and plants.

What follows was carefully written into one of her
notebooks, though whether it was her own or some older
practitioner's composition, I have no means of knowing:

In the book of Ecclesiasticus we read: "The Lord hath
created medicines out of the earth, and he that is wise
will not abhor them." Gypsies, descended from ancient
Egyptian tribes, believe that for every ill we suffer there
is a plant growing somewhere to cure it.

They used the herbs of the fields and hedgerows, and
the homely ones growing in their cottage gardens. They
ate sage leaves with their daily bread and cheese, for it
was said: "How can a man die with sage in his garden?"
They drank good nettle ale, cider and mead.

Wise mothers dosed ailing daughters with the homely mugwort tea, believing the old proverb:

"If they would drink nettles in March
And eat mugwort in May,
So many fine maidens
Wouldn't go to clay."

For perfumes country folk used sweet musk, gilly flowers, cabbage roses, lad's love and rosemary.

* * *

Camomile is a comforting herb. The specific name of this well-known field plant is Anthemis, from anthos, a flower; meaning in this case that it is not only a flower, but one well worthy of notice. It is said that every part of the plant has healing properties.

* * *

Balm tea is another old favourite. Mothers used to give it to lazy children because it was said to stimulate them.

* * *

Young nettles grow thickly everywhere in the Spring. Herbalists claim there is no Spring medicine so purifying for the blood.

* * *

Coltsfoot is another prolific herb, appearing early in the year. This plant has been used for centuries as a remedy for Spring coughs. It was so well thought of that apothecaries honoured it by painting its flowers on the doorposts of their shops. Its leaves, shaped like a colt's foot, were dried and used as tobacco, while its silky, white seeds were collected by housewives as pillow stuffing.

* * *

Dandelion is very valuable for diseases of heart and liver. It was sometimes called "heart-fever grass." Its young leaves give flavour and goodness to salads.

* * *

For many, many centuries, the elder has been a famous

medicine, believed to cure everything. Country folk looked upon elder as a sort of apothecary's shop conveniently growing in the hedgerows. Its flowers, leaves and berries, made into cordials, teas, and wines, were drunk hot at bedtime to cure colds. Most of us know Hans Andersen's story of the little boy who got his feet wet—"The Elder Tree Mother."

The boy's mother put him to bed and into a teapot she put some elder flowers to make a warm, comforting cup of elder tea: "The little boy looked at the teapot; he saw the lid rise and the elder flowers spring forth, so fresh and white they were, and they shot out long, thick branches—even out of the spout they shot forth—spreading on all sides, and growing larger and larger, till at last there stood by the bedside a most charming elder bush, a perfect tree, some of its branches stretching over the bed and thrusting the curtain aside. Oh, how full of blossoms was this tree, and how fragrant were those blossoms! And in the midst of the tree sat a kind-looking old dame, wearing the strangest dress in the world. It was green like the elder leaves, with a pattern of large white elder flower clusters spreading all over it—one could not be sure whether it was actually a gown or real, living green leaves and flowers."

The Tree-Eaters

Slippery elm—as a healing nourishing food—was discovered by early colonists in North America. They knew little of the terrible, long winters in that country, and when the first frost came they hadn't enough food and faced starvation. They had to eat roots and gnaw the bark of trees. One of the trees was the Canadian elm, and the people who ate this bark found that it not only satisfied their hunger, but gave them strength and vigour.

Although we are told there is healing in every herb that grows, it is dangerous to experiment with them. The herbalist, learning his art, must be wary, and never taste the berries, or any part of a plant, unless its properties are known to him, for certain parts of healing plants are often poisonous.

Balm was popular as a physic herb and for its sweet scent, and was also used for rubbing on furniture to pleasantly perfume a house. In "The Merry Wives of Windsor," Anne Page bids the elves:

"The several chairs of order look you scour
With juice of balm and every precious flower."

Decoctions

The usual method of giving a herbal medicine is by means of what is known as a decoction. To make decoctions, herbs are simply boiled in water. They should be prepared fresh daily. Sometimes herbs and water are boiled, strained and the liquor used to cover fresh herbs and again boiled. Decoctions should be made over a clear flame, free from smoke, in a covered vessel; and, in the case of herb leaves, brought to the boil, then strained into a jug and covered till cold.

Decoctions are solutions of the active principles of vegetable substances obtained by boiling. This method is adopted to obtain principles which cannot be separated by simple infusion in cold or even boiling water. Small quantities only should be made at a time, as they are apt to change.

Decoction of oak bark—Take an ounce of oak bark and a pint of water. Put into a covered vessel and boil for 10 minutes, then strain. The dose of this preparation is from 2 to 6 tablespoonsful. It is a fine astringent, and used as a gargle for relaxed throat.

Decoction of barley—Take 2 oz. pearl barley and 5 pints of water. Wash the barley in cold water, reject the washings, and having poured over it half-a-pint of water, boil for 5 minutes. Repeat, then after adding the remainder of the water boiling, let the whole boil down to 2 pints, then strain. Barley water made this way is serviceable in all cases of fever and inflammation, and can be taken in any quantity. To this, various substances are sometimes added, such as sliced figs, raisins, liquorice root, slices of lemon, and sugar-candy.

*   *   *

Decoctions are valuable for illnesses connected with stomach, bowels and kidneys, because this fluid passes quicker into these organs than any other medicine. They can be sweetened with sugar but are better without. If roots, barks, leaves, flowers and seeds are boiled together, let the roots boil first for some time, then add the bark and bring to the boil again; and so with leaves, seeds and flowers, each in the order mentioned. Figs, quince seeds, and linseed, should be tied in a muslin bag—all need long boiling—then should be removed before straining the liquid. Decoctions must be kept covered. The usual dose is from 1 to 5 liquid ounces, according to the strength of the decoction and the age of the patient.

Rosemary Decoction

A decoction of rosemary, made with wine instead of water, used to be taken as a remedy against giddiness. A decoction of a good handful of the leaves, covered with cold water, brought to the boil and strained, is an excellent hair tonic to be rubbed into the scalp till the skin glows.

Balm

A stimulant for use in fevers, you should try a compound spirit of balm. This spirit—almost as good as a liqueur—is distilled from 8 oz. of balm, 4 oz. of lemon peel, 2 oz. each of nutmeg and carraway seeds, and 1 oz. each of angelica root, cinnamon and cloves. Add a quart of brandy, keep the liqueur in stoppered bottles, and use as a stimulant.

Infusion of balm is prepared by covering an ounce of leaves with one pint of boiling water, and letting it stand for 15 minutes.

Strain, then take freely in wine-glassful doses as a tonic, and to induce perspiration.

Beans

Are good for a variety of ailments. For boils, reduce haricot beans to a powder, mix with an equal quantity of fenugreek and honey, and apply outwardly to boils, bruises, or blue marks caused by a blow.

You can also usefully treat eye troubles with beans. Mix bean flour with equal quantities of rose leaves, frankincense and the white of an egg. Apply to eyes that water or are swollen.

Sciatica can be eased by burning bean husks to ashes, and mixing into an ointment with unsalted lard. Apply for old pains, sciatica, and gout.

Celery

This is excellent for rheumatism. Cut celery into pieces and boil in water until soft, then drink the water. Put new milk, with a little flour and nutmeg, into a saucepan with boiled celery, and serve warm with pieces of toast. Eat with potatoes, and the rheumatic aches and pains will ease.

Camomile Lotion—*for skin and hair*

Place 5 or 6 dried camomile flowers in a bowl and pour a half-pint of boiling water over them. Cover the bowl for 10 or 12 minutes. When the lotion has slightly cooled, sponge it on the skin with a small pad of cotton wool. Camomile lotion is credited with astringent properties, is used for closing enlarged pores and toning-up relaxed muscles. This lotion also makes an excellent hair tonic. Cleanse the scalp with it twice a week.

Cold Cream

To make a simple cold cream, take 1½ oz. olive oil, 6 drachms of white wax, 2 drachms of spermacetti, and 3 drops of oil of lavender. Melt the wax and spermacetti in the oil in a double saucepan or a jar standing in a pan of boiling water over a flame. Stir vigorously with a porcelain or bone spoon until the ointment is well mixed. Remove from the fire and beat gently until it becomes stiff and sets, when it should be potted for use.

Coltsfoot

Coltsfoot syrup is a first-class remedy for coughs, colds, giddiness and headache.

For coughs and colds make a decoction from a handful of the leaves in 2 pints of water. Boil down to 1 pint, strain and sweeten with a syrup made of sugar-candy. The dose is an occasional teacupful.

Dandelion

Dandelion extract acts on the liver and has a slight aperient action.

Boil down a decoction of the *fresh* root, sliced—1 oz. to 1 pint of water—to half-a-pint, and strain; add 2 drachms of cream of tartar. Dose: a wine-glassful taken two or three times daily.

An excellent liver tonic is made with 4 oz. of fresh dandelion roots boiled in 2 pints of water until the liquid is reduced to 1 pint. Strain off and take a wine-glassful twice a day.

This is also good for rheumatism.

Ointment for Obstinate Ulcers

Bruise a pound of primrose leaves with half-a-pound of the flowers, simmer them in an equal quantity of lard without salt until the primroses become crisp, then strain through a coarse sieve.

Elecampane

This root is aromatic, tonic, and stimulating. It is used for dyspepsia and pulmonary affections.

The infusion of elecampane is made from the dried root covered with boiling water.

Dosage is 1 fluid ounce.

Hart's Tongue

A cure for hiccough. The distilled water of the hart's tongue fern is good for stopping hiccough. Used as a gargle, it cures bleeding gums.

Lotion for Soothing Heat and Skin Irritation

2 oz. lettuce juice, 2 drs. of Eau de Cologne, 2 oz. distilled vinegar, 4 oz. elder flower water, well mixed. Dab the skin with it frequently.

Lotion to Soothe General Body Irritation

Bathe with grains of boracic acid diluted with an ounce of water, and powder with talcum powder.

Linseed Lotion

For unbroken chilblains and rheumatism, apply lotion made of 4 tablespoonsful each of pure linseed oil, and oil of turpentine. Add 2 drachms of spirits of camphor and shake well until mixed.

Marshmallow Ointment

Highly prized for soothing effects and for allaying inflammations. Made by macerating equal weights of marshmallow leaves and pure unsalted lard together in a double saucepan, or jar standing in a pan of boiling water. Simmer for an hour to extract all soluble parts of the leaves before the ointment is strained and potted.

Or, you can boil the leaves for 45 minutes, strain and evaporate the liquid to a thin extract, and then mix with lard.

Physicians rarely take medicine

'Tis the great Art of Life to manage well the restless mind

The surest way to health, say what they will
Is never to suppose we shall be ill
Most of those evils we poor mortals know
From doctors and imagination flow

A man as he manages himself may die old at thirty, or young at eighty

God and the doctor we alike adore
But only when in danger, not before
The danger o'er, both are alike requited
God is forgotten and the doctor slighted

Children and chickens must be always picking

The head and feet keep warm; the rest will take no harm

4

Grannie's Invalid Diets

Arrowroot

TAKE a tablespoonful of arrowroot and mix into thin paste with a little water. Gradually add half-a-pint of boiling water, stirring the whole time. Put on the stove for 3 or 4 minutes, continuing to stir until the whole is evenly mixed.

Remove from the stove and add grated nutmeg, sugar, etc., to taste. A little lemon juice is an effective alternative to the nutmeg. It is more nourishing if made with milk, but it can be too rich for a weak stomach, then water is preferable. It should always be prepared fresh as required.

Although arrowroot is a valuable and easily digestible food for invalids and children, remember that it isn't very nourishing.

"As a vehicle for wine," said Miss Florence Nightingale, "and as a restorative quickly prepared, it is all very well. But it is nothing but starch and water. Flour is both more nutritive and less liable to ferment, and is preferable wherever it can be used."

Arrowroot Pudding

Rub a tablespoonful of arrowroot in a basin with a little cold water, and add, stirring constantly, a pint of boiling milk. Mix in the contents of one egg and three teaspoonsful of powdered, refined sugar, which have previously been beaten together. Boil in a basin, or bake. This is good for early convalescence.

Arrowroot Blancmange

Take three tablespoonsful of arrowroot, make into a mucilage with water, then add milk in sufficient quantity, and boil until of a proper consistence. Pour into a mould, and allow to cool and set. Eat with currant jelly or with lemon juice and sugar. Milk or beef-tea may be used instead of water in the preparation of arrowroot mucilage. It should be boiled 20 minutes. This again is excellent for early convalescence.

Arrowroot-water

Take 2 teaspoonsful of arrowroot, and make into a smooth paste with a little water. Add a pint of water, and simmer for 5 minutes, stirring constantly.

Strengthening Jelly

Soak overnight 2 oz. of isinglass or prepared gelatine, 1 oz. of gum arabic, 5 oz. of sugar-candy, and a grated nutmeg in a bottle of port wine. In the morning, simmer on stove till dissolved. Strain and set aside in a cool place till it forms firm jelly. A piece the size of a nutmeg may be taken 5 or 6 times a day. This is good for debility when the stomach is unable to bear normal food.

Strawberry Tea

Strawberries contain citric acid, and "strawberry treatment" is said to be effective for gout, stone in the bladder, kidney trouble, worms in the intestines.

In fever cases, strawberries squeezed in water make a cooling, refreshing beverage. Delightful-tasting tea can be made from dried leaves of the wild strawberry. May and June are the best months to collect the leaves. At the same time, collect young blackberry leaves and young wood-roof leaves, and dry in the same way as the strawberry leaves. From a mixture of these three kinds of leaves you can produce a drink equal in taste and aroma to Chinese tea.

Young blackberry leaves possess the same taste as pure, good Chinese tea, and better than most other teas. Leaves must be put in a dry place, not in the sun, then stored for use in a closed jar. To make about 6 cups of tea, use as much as can be taken up with the tips of the fingers of one hand. Pour boiling water on it, and leave for 5 or 10 minutes. Add a little sugar, but no milk, and you have a very pleasant-tasting drink.

Honey

Honey is an excellent "pick-me-up" for older folk. It is laxative, purifying, strengthening. Mixed with tea, it is a remedy for catarrh and phlegm. It is also good for external sores if you take half-parts of honey and flour, and mix well together by adding a little water. Honey ointment should be thick, not fluid. Used internally, honey acts efficaciously in many other ailments.

If difficulty of swallowing is felt, boil a teaspoonful of honey with half-a-pint of water. This makes a delicious throat-gargle for singers; and if a drop is swallowed, there is no risk of tummy upset.

Honey-water is wonderful for the eyes as a purifier

and strengthener. Boil a teaspoonful of honey in half-a-pint of water for 5 minutes, and the decotion is ready for use.

Grandmother knew a man of over eighty who added a teaspoonful of pure honey to some boiling water, and allowed it to boil for a time. He soon had a tasty wine which was also invigorating. He used to say: "I owe my strength and vigorous old age to honey-wine." Its effects are aperient, purifying, nourishing and invigorating. It is reminiscent of the "mead" of ancient times.

Honey is excellent for healing ulcerated throat. Boil a spoonful of honey with two pints of water for a few minutes, then take 2 to 4 spoonsful of it every hour.

Half-a-spoonful of coriander boiled with a spoonful of honey in 2 pints of water. A spoonful taken hourly cleanses the stomach.

Weak, delicate children should be given a cupful or two of boiled milk daily to which has been added a little honey. Never use raw honey for a cough as it can be too sharp, but if boiled in either water or milk, the cough will be soothed or clear up completely.

Brandy Mixture

Take brandy and water—4 tablespoonsful each; 2 egg yolks, and a half-ounce of powdered white sugar. Beat the yolks and sugar together; add the spirit and water, flavour with grated cinnamon or nutmeg and you have a stimulant and restorative for anyone feeling run-down.

Adult dose is from one to three tablespoonsful repeated according to need. Children should be given a teaspoonful to a tablespoonful according to age.

White Wine Whey

Take a pint of milk, add mace, nutmeg and cinnamon, with sugar to taste. Boil until the milk is on the point of boiling. Remove and add in one or two wine-glassfuls of sherry or white wine. Put back on the boil, stirring gently one way until it curdles. Remove, and strain through a teacloth or some muslin. Make sure the patient is warmly tucked in bed, give him the White Wine Whey and it will make him perspire profusely. This is excellent for catarrh and influenza.

Wine Whey

Pour half-a-pint of sherry to a pint of boiling milk; stir thoroughly until it coagulates. Strain off the whey, and sweeten to taste.

Egg Nog

Beat an egg yolk with 6 oz. of milk. Add some brandy or whisky, and some sugar. Add a beaten egg white.

A tablespoonful of lime-water added to Wine Whey and Egg Nog makes them more easily digestible.

Egg Jelly

Take 3 new-laid eggs; separate whites from yolks, and beat separately. Dissolve half-an-ounce of isinglass in a quarter-pint of warm water and add the juice of half a lemon. Mix together and add 2 tablespoonsful of brandy. Pour into a mould, and cool.

Pish-Pash

For invalids, it comprises fresh meat cooked in rice. Cut a chicken into small pieces, place in a small pan, add 3 tablespoonsful of rice. Pour over it 2 breakfast-cupsful of cold water, and cook slowly. You can add spices during cooking. The rice part alone, which will have absorbed most of the strength of the meat, can be used if the patient is very ill.

Water-Souchy

Take 2 flounders, soles, whitings, or haddocks, and boil in a quart of water so that the fish are reduced to pulp. Strain, and removing the fins from 4 more fish, put them into the liquid. Add salt and cayenne pepper to taste and a little chopped parsley. Boil well and eat with the sauce. This is very digestible.

Macaroni Pudding

To 4 tablespoonsful of cinnamon water add 2 oz. macaroni. Simmer until the macaroni is tender. Add 3 egg yolks, white of an egg, an ounce sugar, drop of oil of bitter almonds, a glass of raisin wine, beaten into half-a-pint of milk. Bake in a slow oven.

Rice Pudding

Add 2 tablespoonsful of rice to a pint-and-a-half of milk and simmer until the rice is soft. Add 2 eggs, beaten with half-an-ounce of sugar. Bake for three quarters-of-an-hour in the oven.

Rice and Apples

Take some rice and boil quickly in hot water. Strain through a colander; expose for 15 minutes. Stew separately some apples; mix with the rice and sweeten to taste.

Rennet-Whey

Take a piece of rennet and infuse it in some boiling water, removing all soluble matter. After pouring off the liquid, take a tablespoonful of it, and mix with 3 tablespoonsful of milk. Place the mixture near heat, covering with a piece of clean cloth. When a uniform curd forms, remove it, divide into small pieces with a spoon, and separate the whey with gentle pressure. This is good for feverish conditions.

White Wine Whey

Put a-half-pint of new milk into a deep pan. Place on the stove and as soon as scum rises to the edge of the pan, pour in a glass of sherry, or other white wine, then sweeten with a teaspoonful of refined sugar. Boil again, stirring constantly, then place aside until the curd forms a lump. Strain the whey through a sieve or piece of muslin. It can be taken cold or tepid and is an excellent moderate stimulant.

Egg Brandy

Take 3 eggs and beat them with 5 oz. plain water. Slowly add 3 oz. of brandy, also a little sugar and nutmeg. Two tablespoonsful of this can be given at a time. This is good for prostration cases.

Another useful stimulant is made by taking the white of a new-laid egg and stirring with a tablespoonful of cream. Add a tablespoonful of brandy in which a lump of sugar has been dissolved.

Milk and Soda Water

Sweeten half-a-pint of milk with a teaspoonful of refined sugar. Bring almost to boiling point and pour over it a bottle of soda water. For stomach acidity, this is the way to administer milk.

Boiled Flour and Milk

Wheaten flour, kneaded with water, is put into a linen cloth and tied firmly. Next place in a pan of water and boil slowly for 12 hours. Dry, then take the thick rind away on removing the cloth, and again dry. A tablespoonful of this grated and boiled with a pint of milk, is excellent for recovery from diarrhoea or dysentery.

Boiled Bread Pudding

Pour a pint of hot milk over half-a-pound stale bread, and allow the mixture to soak for an hour in a covered basin. Beat with 2 eggs. Put it all into a covered basin, tie a cloth over it, and place in boiling water for half-an-hour. Eat with salt or sugar.

Batter Pudding

Beat the contents of 2 eggs with half-an-ounce of sugar. Mix this with a tablespoonful of wheaten flour and a pint of milk. Put in a basin of boiling water and boil with a cloth tied over it.

Tapioca Pudding

Make a pint of tapioca mucilage with milk. Beat 2 egg yolks with half-an-ounce of sugar, and stir into the mucilage. Bake in a slow oven. Sago and arrowroot can be made into similar puddings.

Mashed Carrots and Turnips

Peel the carrots and turnips; boil separately in 3 successive waters; press the water out through a clear, coarse cloth, mash together with sufficient milk to make into a pulp. Season with salt. Place before heat till the surface dries.

Vermicelli, or Macaroni Soup

To a quart of beef-tea boiled to a third, add an ounce of vermicelli or 2 oz. of macaroni previously well boiled in water. Boil the whole to one pint. Add salt to taste. Instead of vermicelli or macaroni, you can use rice. It should be added to the soup after its concentration. Previously prepare the rice by boiling and slightly drying.

Chicken Broth

Beat the yolk of an egg with 2 oz. of water. Add with parsley or celery to chicken tea, and boil to a half. Rice, vermicelli, or macaroni, fully boiled, can be mixed in.

Mutton Broth with Vegetables

Slowly boil in a pan for 2 hours a pound of fat-free mutton chops. Remove the chops, and to the remainder add 3 carrots and 3 turnips, peeled, sliced, boiled, with the water drained, plus 2 onions, sliced and boiled. Season with salt and celery. Simmer slowly for 4 hours. Put the chops in again, and simmer for another hour.

Tripe

Boil some onions in 2 waters, and partially boil some tripe. Boil together slowly till the tripe is soft and tender. Add salt and a few grains of cayenne pepper. Tripe is easily digested and very good for a convalescent.

Grit-gruel

Wash grits in cold water. Pour off the fluid and add fresh cold water. Boil slowly, until the water is reduced by half. Strain through a sieve. An ounce-and-a-half of grits should make a pint of gruel.

Oatmeal Gruel

Take 2 or 3 tablespoonsful of oatmeal and rub in a basin with a little cold water. Repeat the process, adding fresh water each time until milkiness stops reaching the water. Put the washings into a pan, and boil till a thick mucilage forms. These gruels contain more nourishment than sago, arrowroot, or tapioca, as they contain a small quantity of gluten. Sweeten and mix with milk, if preferred.

Iceland Moss Jelly

Iceland moss contains a bitter principle which should be cleared before use. To do this, pound dry; soak in tepid water with a little bicarbonate of soda for 24 hours, then press in a coarse cloth. Add an ounce of the prepared moss to a quart of water and let the mixture boil to a half. Strain through a sieve, and sweeten, or mix with milk, according to taste.

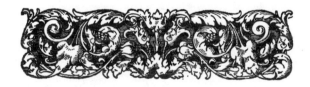

More die by food than famine

Diet cures more than the lancet

Feed sparingly and defy the physician

Cheese is a peevish elf:
It digests everything but itself

We seldom repent of having eaten too little

Better lose a supper than gain a hundred physicians

Many a pie has cost an industrious husband a twenty-pound note in doctor's bills; and many a human life has paid for an apple dumpling

Over exertion, or anxiety of mind, disturbs digestion infinitely more than fatigue of body—the brain demands a much more abundant supply of the animal spirits than is required for the excitement of mere legs and arms

5

Grannie's
Invalid
Drinks

Invalid Orgeat

BEAT 2 oz. of almonds with a teaspoonful of organe-flower water and a bitter almond or two. Pour a quart of milk and water to the paste. Sweeten with sugar or capillaire. This is good for those with a tender chest. It is also good for gout. By adding half-an-ounce gum arabic, it allays the pain.

Cranberry Drink

Mash a teacupful of cranberries into a cup of water. Boil 2 quarts of water with a large spoonful of oatmeal and a bit of lemon peel. Add the cranberries and some sugar, then about ¼ pint of sherry, or less. Boil the whole for half-an-hour and strain off.

Egg Milks

Beat a fresh-laid egg, and mix well with ¼-pint of warm

milk, a tablespoonful of capillaire, the same of rosewater, and a little scraped nutmeg. Do not warm it after the egg is mixed in. Take first thing in the morning and last thing at night and it will be found strengthening and particularly helpful for anyone suffering from a cough.

Add the beaten yolks of 3 eggs to 2 tablespoonsful of powdered white sugar, 3 cloves, the rind of half-a-lemon, and half-a-pint brandy. Pour over it a quart of warm milk, stirring rapidly. Serve immediately.

Convalescent Strengthening Drink

Beat an egg white to a froth, then beat the yolk in a table-spoonful of cold water. Put a tablespoonful of cold water in a wineglass, add a tablespoonful of sherry, then make it hot. Pour in the egg, stir constantly, put in a saucepan and on a slow flame. Stir one way till it thickens. Do not let it boil. When hot, put in the whipped white to set. The drink can be taken hot or cold.

Parsley Tea

Stimulates the kidneys and is good for rheumatism. Take a handful of freshly gathered leaves or a tablespoonful of dried parsley, and wash in cold running water. Put into an earthenware jug and pour over a pint of boiling water. Cover the jug with a cloth. Let it get cold, then strain into a glass jug. Drink plenty of it an hour before meals.

Peppermint Tea

Infuse a large handful of mint leaves in $\frac{1}{2}$-pint of boiling water, then add a teaspoonful of honey. A wine-glassful taken hot at bedtime is excellent for a cold.

For cases of nausea and flatulence, add an ounce of mint leaves to a pint of boiling water. Let stand till cold, strain, and take a wine-glassful frequently.

Betany Tea

Gathered when about to flower, Betany has the taste of tea when brewed the same way. It cures headaches.

Hawthorn Tea

Mix hawthorn leaves together with one part of balm and sage. They make an excellent and pleasant sanative tea, particularly good for nervous people.

Irish Moss Jelly

An ounce of carrageen, or Irish moss, should be boiled in a pint-and-a-half water, then sweeten and acidulate, or mix with milk as in Iceland Moss Jelly.

Ground Rice Milk

Mix a tablespoonful of ground rice with a pint-and-a-half milk, add half-an-ounce candied lemon-peel cut into slices, boil for half-an-hour; strain while hot. This is nutritious during acute disease and early convalescence.

Rice Milk

Boil a tablespoonful of ground rice with a pint-and-a-half milk, or equal parts of milk and water. Stir smooth, and boil 2 minutes. Flavour with sugar and nutmeg. Very nourishing for children.

Bread Panada

Grate a piece of stale bread and mix into sufficient water to form a thick pulp. Cover, and after it has soaked an hour, beat with 2 tablespoonsful of milk and a little sugar, then boil for 10 minutes, stirring constantly.

Sago

Add a tablespoonful of the best sago to a pint of water, and let it stand for two hours, then boil for a quarter-of-an-hour, stirring constantly until it forms a clear, uniform jelly.

Remove from the stove, and flavour with sugar, nutmeg, as in the case of arrowroot. Instead of water you can use milk. Sago is frequently employed where a non-stimulating diet is required.

Sago Milk

Soak an ounce of sago in a pint of water for an hour. Pour off the water and add a pint-and-a-half milk. Boil slowly until the sago is well incorporated with the milk.

Sago Posset

Put 2 tablespoonsful of sago into a pint of water and boil until a mucilage forms. Take lemon rind and rub a quarter-ounce of loaf sugar on it. Put in with half-a-teaspoonful of tincture of ginger into 5 oz. of sherry wine. Add the mixture to the sago mucilage and boil 5 minutes. A wine-glassful may be taken at a time and is excellent for debility from acute diseases of a non-inflammatory nature.

Tapioca

Prepare the same as sago, only, being more soluble in water, it requires half the time for maceration and boiling. Sweeten and flavour like sago.

Tous-les-mois

This should be prepared like arrowroot. It has the same value.

Motherwort Tea

A full tablespoonful of dried motherwort should be put in a jug and poured over a cupful of boiling water. Cover the jug with a cloth and leave to cool. Strain, then divide into two doses and take at half-hour intervals. This is a good stimulant for tired mental workers.

Sage Tea

Boil equal parts of sage, rosemary, honeysuckle and plantain in water. Be sure the water covers. Add a tablespoonful of honey to each pint of liquid and use as required. This makes a good hairwash; a gargle for sore throat, or will heal a sore mouth.

Yarrow Tea

Brew as you would ordinary tea with a tablespoonful each of dried leaves mixed with dried elder-flowers. Drink hot on retiring if you have a bad cold.

Lime Water

Excellent to give children with their milk when there is tendency to acidity, or when the bowels are too relaxed. A tablespoonful should be mixed with 3 tablespoonsful of milk.

Apple Water

Slice 2 large apples and pour a quart boiling water on them. Strain in 2 or 3 hours, and sweeten with honey.

Linseed Tea

Take 2 drachms of bruised liquorice-root and an ounce of linseed, and put into a pint of boiling water. Allow the jug to stand near a warm stove for 4 hours, then strain through muslin or calico. Don't bruise the linseed. This is good for coughs.

Egg Wine

Beat an egg (yolk and white) with a tablespoonful of cold water. Pour on it a mixture of a glass of sherry or white wine, and half-a-glass of water previously heated together (not boiling), stirring all the time. Sweeten with white sugar, and add a little grated nutmeg, to taste. Taken in this form it is more digestible, but flavour is improved by heating ingredients in saucepan (not to boiling), stirring one way for a minute till they thicken. With a slice of toast or biscuit, this can be advantageously taken by invalids twice daily.

Egg wine, made as above, without warming the egg, is lighter on the stomach, but isn't so pleasant.

Lemon Wheys

Pour as much lemon juice into boiling milk as will make a small quantity quite clear. Dilute with hot water to an agreeable acid, and put in a lump or two of sugar. This promotes perspiration.

Egg Emulsion

Rub a yolk of 2 eggs and a little sugar with a pint of cold

water. Add afterwards a glass of wine and a little lemon juice for flavour. This is very restorative in cases of debility, and for recovery from severe illness when mild stimulation is required. With wine, the emulsion is as good for coughs, hoarseness, and constipation.

Toast and Water

Slowly toast a thin piece of bread until extremely brown and hard. Plunge it into a jug of cold water and cover for an hour before use. It should be a brown colour before drinking and is good for weak bowels.

Toast Water

Toast very brown, one pint of white or brown bread-crusts. Add a pint of cold water, and let stand an hour. Strain, then add cream and sugar.

Apple Tea

Roast 2 large sour apples and cover with boiling water. Cool and strain, pour, and add sugar to taste.

Rice Water

Two tablespoonsful of rice; one quart of cold water; cook an hour, or until dissolved. Add salt and sugar to taste.

Flaxseed Lemonade

Pour a quart of boiling water over 4 tablespoonsful of cold flaxseed. Steep 3 hours, strain, add juice of 3 lemons, and sweeten to taste.

Orange Whey

The juice of an orange to a pint of sweetened milk. Heat slowly until curds form. Strain and cool.

Egg Lemonade

Take the white of an egg, one tablespoonful of pulverised sugar, juice of one lemon, one glass of water, then beat together.

Baked Milk

Put half-a-gallon of milk in a jar, and tie it down with paper. Let it stand in a moderate oven 8 or 10 hours. It will be like cream, and very nutritious.

Cranberry Jelly Juice

Mix cranberry jelly with cold water.

Redcurrant Whisky

For a cold, add a little redcurrant jelly to a glass of hot whisky punch. Drink before going to sleep.

Cooling Draught

Fifteen grs. of sulphate of magnesia, 20 grs. sulphate of soda, 2 drs. syrup of orange peel, and 2 oz. distilled water. Taken every morning before breakfast for a week, soothes skin irritation.

Lemonade

Hot, strong lemonade at bedtime will often break-up a bad cold.

Imperial Drink

To a quart of boiling water add 2 teaspoonsful cream of tartar, the juice of 2 lemons, and sweeten with honey or sugar. It should be ice-cold.

Barley-water

Add one tablespoonful of pearl barley to a pint of water, and boil for a few minutes, stirring constantly to wash the grain. Pour off the water, and add one pint-and-a-half of clean water; simmer gently for an hour, and strain. Sugar and lemon juice may be added. Extremely good for colds and other illnesses.

Beef Essence

Take a pound of gravy beef, free from skin and fat, and chop fine. Mix with 3 tablespoonsful of water and pound it.

Allow to soak for 2 hours. Put into a covered earthen jar with a little salt. The edges of the jar should be sealed and a cloth tied over the top. The jar should be placed in a pot half-full of boiling water, and kept on the stove 4 hours. Now strain through a coarse sieve, so that the fluid and the smaller solid particles of the meat can pass. Two teaspoonsful or more can be given at a time for serious debility.

Beef Tea

Take a pound of beefsteak or gravy beef free from fat; mince or cut into small pieces; put in a well-covered jar with a pint-and-a-half of cold water or barley-water. Now place the jar in a saucepan of water and simmer for 3 hours, or leave the jar in a not too hot oven overnight. Strain, and remove fat.

Or, take some good-quality gravy beef or beefsteak, beat well, rub pepper and salt over it, place on a flat tin punched with small holes (an onion grater could be used), pour some port wine over the meat, then cover with a plate and place some weights on it.

Increase the weights a couple of times to help press all the juice from the meat.

Chicken Tea

Take a small chicken. Remove the skin and fat between the muscles, divided into two long halves. Remove the lungs and everything adhering to the backbone and chest walls; cut into thin slices. Place the slices in a pan with some salt, then pour over it a quart of boiling water. Cover the pan and boil slowly 2 hours. Allow to stand for half-an-hour, strain off the fluid through a sieve. Beef-tea and chicken-tea are excellent during sickness if animal diet is admissible, and, by adding flour, or other thickening substance, are good convalescence nourishment.

Mutton Tea

A pound of mutton, free from fat, should be cut into thin slices. Pour a pint-and-a-half of water over it, allowing it to macerate, as in beef-tea. Afterward, boil for half-an-hour and strain.

Veal Tea

A pound of fillet of veal, free from fat, should be sliced, then boiled for half-an-hour in a pint-and-a-half of boiling water.

Stokos

Put ¾ lb. fine oatmeal, 6 oz. sugar, and half-a-lemon cut into slices into a pan. Mix together with a little warm water. Add a gallon of boiling water, stir thoroughly, and use cold. This is a very nourishing drink, as is the next suggestion.

Cokos

Mix into a thin batter 6 oz. of sugar, 6 oz. of fine oatmeal, 4 oz. of cocoa. Add a gallon boiling water; put into a stone bottle and cork. This is a very good drink after strenuous athletics or exercise.

Mustard Bath

And, for the convalescent, a *mustard bath* is also an excellent stimulant. Two tablespoonsful of mustard are required for every gallon of water in the bath. The mustard should first be made into a paste in a basin, then gradually added to the water in the bath. Temperature 100° F.

Eat a bit before you drink

Be temperate in all things

Eat at pleasure, drink by measure

He that goes to bed thirsty rises healthy

Temperance is reason's girdle and passion's bridle

The intemperate die young and rarely enjoy old age

*Against diseases here the strongest fence
Is the defensive virtue abstinence*

All sick people want to get well, but not always in the best way. Said a wealthy man, Doctor, strike at the root of the disease, and smash went the decanter under the faithful physician's cane

6

Grannie's
Keep-Fit Rules

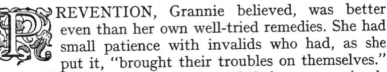REVENTION, Grannie believed, was better
even than her own well-tried remedies. She had
small patience with invalids who had, as she
put it, "brought their troubles on themselves."
Her favourite rules, as she recorded them, were simple
and effective.

Hints for Health

Never lean the back against anything cold.

Never begin a journey till breakfast has been eaten.

Never take warm drinks and go straight into the cold.

Keep the back, especially between the shoulders, well-
covered, and the chest well protected.

Never go to bed with cold or wet feet.

Bathe daily to keep the skin in active condition, and the pores well open.

Never ride in an open carriage or on a bicycle when warm from exercise.

When hoarse, speak as little as possible until the hoarseness has gone.

When sleeping in a cold place, breathe through the nose, and keep your mouth shut.

When going from a hot atmosphere into a cold one, keep the mouth closed so that the air may be warmed in ·its passage through the nose before it reaches the lungs.

Never stand on ice or snow where there is too much exposure to cold wind.

Never stand still in cold weather, especially after exercise.

When sewing or writing, change position from time to time.

*   *   *

My grandmother used to tell me of the experiences of a Mr. George Catlin, an American artist. During years of association with American Indian tribes, he concluded that one of the main causes of ailments affecting civilised peoples is their habit of breathing through the mouth.

The Indian child, he observed, was never allowed to sleep with its mouth open. The mother always pressed the baby's lips together as soon as it fell asleep, to form a lasting habit. So, when the child grew, sleeping or waking, it kept its mouth shut. Mr. Catlin claimed that this habit was the reason why native races of North and South America used to enjoy such good physical perfection and escape so many of the diseases of civilised communities. Among millions of natives, he never saw or heard of a hunchback or crooked spine, or an idiot or lunatic, and premature death was also uncommon.

It is plain that nostrils are for breathing, and are the natural outlet of the lungs. The sides of the air passages are lined with hairs which, to some degree, prevent ingress of noxious matters. You are healthier if you breathe through the nose. Some people who lived in malarious districts for years without suffering from any of the fevers that haunt such neighbourhoods, ascribe their exemption entirely to the habit of breathing properly. Air comes in contact with the membranes of the nose, and these are supposed to have some power of neutralising malarious and contagious poisons. It is also to be noticed that, by drawing in our breath only through the nostrils, the air is warmed by contact with the membranes before it reaches the lungs, and so inflammation and congestion of these organs are avoided.

Perfect sleep cannot be obtained with the mouth open. "Contrast," said Mr. Catlin, "the natural repose of the Indian child, educated to keep its lips closed, with the uncomfortable slumbers of the child of civilisation, with its little mouth wide open and gasping for breath. The firmly shut mouth, too, promotes good looks. Who ever yet saw an open mouth that was not insipid and unattractive? Keep your mouth shut, then, when you read, when you write, when you listen, when you are in pain, when you are walking, when you are running, and by all means when you are angry."

All crooked or constrained bodily positions affect respiration. Reading, writing, sitting, standing, speaking, or working with the trunk of the body bent forward is extremely hurtful, by overstretching the muscles of the back, compressing the lungs, and pushing downward and backward the stomach, bowels, and abdominal muscles.

There is no time of life at which warmth is of more

importance than in infancy. To plunge a child into cold water, with the idea of making it hardy, as is done in some countries, and even in our own, by some ignorant people, is the height of cruelty and folly. Bowel complaints, croup, and convulsions are likely to result.

A baby should be kept at a temperature above what is suitable for an adult. It should be warmly, but not heavily, clothed.

The room in which it is kept should be maintained at a good but not oppressive heat, and it should never be put into other than tepid water.

Sea-sickness

To prevent sea-sickness, eat well before starting. If sickness comes, it is far better not to retch on an empty stomach. When sea-sickness is prolonged, one of the safest things to take is the white of an egg, beaten in cold water. This will pave the way for a whole egg, with the addition of a little brandy.

Bovril is also good and also, with Brand's essence of chicken, to eat cold.

There's nothing better than antipyrine tablets. Don't take too many, and choose a seat near the centre of the craft to prevent sea-sickness. A teaspoonful of Worcester sauce often relieves.

Cucaine is also very good for sea-sickness. A teaspoonful of a solution of cucaine of the strength of one-in-a-thousand, administered every 2 or 3 hours. For children, give half-drachm doses.

Slimming

To slim, it is necessary to reverse the process by which slim persons become fat. The main principle is withdrawal from the diet of food, such as bread, potatoes, sugar, fat and butter. But diminish the quantities, not suddenly leave off anything to which you have been accustomed for years.

Here is a good diet to follow:

Breakfast (about 8.30 a.m.): Four or 5 ounces of kidneys, boiled fish, bacon, or cold meat (pork or veal excepted), or 2 eggs (not hard-boiled), a large cup of tea or coffee (with neither milk nor sugar), a little biscuit, or an ounce of dried toast, brown bread, or crust off a loaf.

Lunch (about 1 p.m.): Five or 6 ounces of fish (any sort, except salmon, herrings, or eels), any meat (pork or veal excepted), any vegetable (except potatoes, parsnips, beetroot, turnips or carrots), an ounce of dry toast, a crust cut from the loaf, fruit out of the pudding (omit the sugar), any kind of game or poultry, and 2 glasses of dry sherry, or 3 of good, sound claret (no champagne, port or beer to be taken).

Tea (about 5 p.m.): Two or 3 ounces of fruit, a rusk or two, and a cup of tea (without milk or sugar).

Dinner (about 8.30 p.m.): Three or 4 ounces of fish or meat, and a glass or two of wine, if you like.

It is always well for the busy man, who has rushed home to his dinner, to pause a quarter-of-an-hour or so before sitting down to it. Fatigue is not good for digestion.

"A man's body and his mind are like a jerkin and a jerkin's lining; rumple the one, you rumple the other." Brain and stomach must be free from any mutual disturbance, for either to perform functions properly. A state of gentle and pleasurable excitement of the mind is favourable to digestion. "Chatted food," according to the old proverb, "is half digested."

Athletic Training Diet

For athletic training the object is to reduce the fat and

increase the size and hardness of the muscles and the power of endurance. The finest food for athletes is:

Lean and rare beef or mutton
Stale flour bread
Potatoes and other vegetables, in moderation
Tea, coffee, beer or wine, in great moderation.

As this kind of diet contains little or no fat, and little starch or sugar, it cannot feed fatty tissue. Its leading element is nitrogen, which is contained in the beef and mutton. The quantity of tea or coffee allowed is limited to not more than a cup at each meal. Tea is preferable to coffee. Only a glass or two of beer or wine is permissible.

Dyspepsia

To enjoy a good appetite and eat 3 meals a day without discomfort is a blessing, yet millions in good health cannot eat a meal without it being followed by painful dyspepsia. Dyspepsia, grandmother assured us, can be cured, and avoided, by sticking to these rules:

Eat three times a day
No between-meal snacks
Nothing after lunch except a biscuit or slice of bread
    and butter, and a cup of hot drink
Spend at least half-an-hour at each meal
Cut up all the food into small pieces
Never eat so much as to cause the slightest
    uncomfortable sensation afterwards
Try not to work or study hard within half-an-hour
    of eating.

If there is one rule on eating about which most agree, it is that meals should be taken at regular periods. People may differ about what they eat, but you never meet people who say it is as well to take 2 meals today and 5 tomorrow; to take dinner at 1 o'clock today, 3 tomorrow, and 5 next day.

Grandmother used to say that dyspeptics should avoid the following errors: Never weaken the digestive organs by giving them too little to do. Never confine themselves to coarse, loosening foods.

Essential to cure dyspepsia is exercise and particularly out-door exercise.

Those whose health is generally good can cure mild stomach upsets by total abstinence. Abstinence is easily best for disorders arising from indigestion and intemperance.

A king of Persia sent to a tribe of Bedouins a celebrated physician, who inquired how they lived. "We never eat till we are hungry, and then not to repletion," was the answer. "I may retire, then," said the doctor; "I have no business here."

And then there was the famous nobleman who called on a great physician and surgeon. "Doctor, I wish you would examine this eye; I fear some deadly mischief is at work here."

"If you will sit there in my patient's chair, and let me do the talking I will soon find out what is the matter with you." After a few questions, the doctor concluded:

"Your difficulty is not where you think it is, in your eye, but"—pointing his finger at the patient's enormous abdomen—"it is there, in your kitchen. Of course, when the kitchen is out of order, the garret and all the other rooms in the house are likely to be more or less affected. Now all you need to do is to clean the kitchen, and your garret will require no special purification. Your lordship must do as the famous Duke of Wellington did on a well-known occasion—cut off the supplies and the enemy will leave the citadel."

A woman was cured of severe dyspepsia with hard bread and beer. She said: "A German physician was called in; but heart and stomach were on a strike, and refused to assimilate food. In great perplexity, he said: 'Can you take beer?' I could try, and he went on to prescribe:

'You get the General to get you some coot peer, fresh from the prewery. Dake von leetle half-a-glass mit a pit of hart pread and leetle pit uv cheese. Chew de pread slow, and sip de peer. Do not culp it like some beebles do—schust sip schlow, and eat the pread and cheese mit it. I dinks maype dat set de stoomach do vork vonce more!' "

The prescription worked like a charm.

* * *

In the latter part of the last century, a New York man attained so high a reputation for curing dyspepsia that he obtained 500 dollars for each case he undertook, payable in advance. Patients were bound by solemn oath not to reveal his treatment; after his death many, considering themselves free from their obligation, revealed the secret. It mainly consisted in slapping the abdomen or bowels with the palms of the hand for 5 or 10 minutes on rising in the morning; for a quarter-of-an-hour or more about 11 o'clock; in the forenoon, and in the evening before retiring. This is excellent for chronic indigestion. Rubbing and kneading is a very old idea.

In addition to slapping and kneading the abdomen, and exercising freely out of doors, a dyspeptic should eat only when hungry, select digestible food and chew it well. Dyspepsia can also be cured by living on egg yolks beaten with potatoes and water. Try this: Beat an egg in a bowl; add 6 tablespoonsful of cold water; mix the whole together; add 2 tablespoonsful of the farina of potatoes mixed thoroughly with the liquor in the bowl. Pour in as much boiling water as will convert the whole into a jelly. Mix well.

Take it either alone or with a little milk and sugar, not only for breakfast but for stomach debility and at other meals. The dish is light, easily digested, extremely nourishing. Bread or biscuits may be eaten with it as the stomach condition improves.

After dinner sit awhile : after supper walk a mile . . .

Alternate rest and labour long endure

An ounce of prevention is worth a pound of cure

Go to bed with the lamb and rise with the lark

One hour's sleep before midnight is worth two after

Early to bed and early to rise
Make a man healthy, wealthy and wise

The only rule for a rich man to be healthy is by exercise
and abstinence to live as if he were poor

Employment is Nature's physician, and is essential
to human happiness

Be not solitary; be not idle

7

Grannie's
Sickness Remedies

RUNNING through Grannie's legacy of note-books, it is difficult to believe that there was any disease or ailment with which she had not done battle in her time. Some of her remedies were too spartan for inclusion here; a few appear to have no firmer basis than superstition, and the recovery of the patient doubtless owed more to Grannie's firmness of purpose than to her medication. Nevertheless, in the majority of cases, "it worked."

Abscesses and Sores

Make a yeast poultice by mixing 5 oz. of yeast with an equal quantity of hot water; with these stir up a pound of flour to make a poultice, place it on the stove until it swells, then use. This is a stimulating, emollient poultice.

Ankles (sprained)

Take some caraway seeds, pound, and place into a tin basin with a little water. Put on the stove and stir till the mixture thickens, then bind on the ankle. It will ease pain and inflammation.

Or, foment with warm vinegar, 4 or 5 minutes every 4 hours.

Or, shower hot water poured from a few feet over it.

Ankles (weak)

Take a raw oyster in the palm of right hand, and massage the ankles with it until the oyster is almost rubbed away. Do this every evening at bedtime, and the ankles will become stronger.

Asthma

Cut an ounce of stick liquorice into slices. Steep for 24 hours in a quart of water and drink when you are worse than usual.

For asthma, the best drink is apple water—boiling water poured on sliced apples.

Food should be light and easily digestible. Ripe fruits baked, boiled, or roasted, are good; but strong liquor, especially beer or ale, are bad. Supper should be very light.

Baldness

The best baldness preventive is care of the hair during ill-health.

The head should be washed at least once a week. An egg yolk, or a piece of quillaia bark, may be added to the water to produce a lather.

Or, put 4 lb. of unadulterated honey into a still, with 12 handfuls of the tendrils of vines and the same quantity of rosemary-tops. Distil as cool and as slowly as possible.

The liquor may be allowed to drop till it begins to taste sour.

Or, use a pomade made of one part of pilocarpine in 200 parts of petroleum jelly. Regularly used, it will prevent baldness and give great glossiness to the hair.

When the hair is thin, to restore the scalp to a healthy condition, scurf should be cured by bathing with tepid water night and morning, plus the constant application of glycerine and lime-water in between. No fats or oils should be used at this stage as they are liable to go rancid and irritate the scalp still more. Glycerine and lime-water, or fresh olive oil and lime-water, may be used.

A good compound for gentle action on the hair follicles is obtained by adding a few drops of tincture of cantharides to toilet vinegar, then gently damping the scalp after washing well with the compound.

If you are already far gone, you may revive some hair roots by brushing the scalp till redness and a warm glow are produced, then rubbing into the roots of the hair the following lotion: 2 oz. of Eau de Cologne, 2 drs. of tincture of cantharides, 10 drops of oil of lavender, and the same of rosemary. Apply to the head once or twice daily.

Bed-wetting

The child should be prevented from sleeping on its back by threading an empty reel of cotton with tape, and attaching it to the back of the nightdress over the loins. The bed-covering should be light. Iron is beneficial in many cases.

Boils

As soon as a boil appears, bathe it with repeated and continuous applications of ice-cold water, and apply carbolic, camphor, iodine, or solution of caustic. If the boil is obstinate, bring to a head with poultices of camomile flowers.

Boils can result from over-rich diet, or from being run down. For the first, rhubarb, black draught, magnesia, with restricted diet, should be taken. For the second, tonic foods and medicines, soups, fish, eggs, milk, etc., with cod liver oil and mild iron preparations.

Half a wine-glassful of fresh yeast, taken night and morning, often acts like a charm in stopping the formation of fresh crops of boils.

A grain of sulphide of calcium, taken three times a day as a pill, is good.

The boils should be frequently bathed with very hot water, or painted with tincture of iodine or glycerine of belladonna, once or twice daily. If this doesn't succeed, constant poulticing is needed to bring them to a head. After breaking, they should be covered with a piece of lint thickly smeared with salicylic ointment, and fomented frequently with hot water.

Body Odour

Wash twice a day with carbolic or coal tar soap, dry, then dust with boracic acid. The powder should be thoroughly rubbed into the skin. Change stockings twice a day, and they should be dipped in boracic lotion and hung to dry. Inside of shoe and the feet of the stockings should be freely dusted with boracic whenever they are worn. If perspiration is profuse, cork-soles should be worn inside your shoes. The soles should be soaked in boracic lotion, then dried. An iron tonic is also helpful.

Bowel Complaints

A little camphor dissolved with a little clove oil is an excellent remedy for incipient bowel complaints. Repeated doses of a few drops at a time should be taken.

Breath

Rinse mouth and throat with 10 grs. of carbolic acid to

1 oz. of water, 1 dr. each of tincture of calamus and tincture orris root, 1 oz. spirit of nutmeg and 2 oz. of rosewater. For impure breath arising from weakness, a tonic should be taken as well; made of equal parts of wild cherry and cinchona bark.

For acidity of stomach causing bad breath, drink a glass of cold water every morning before getting out of bed, and a glass of hot water before going to bed at night. Rinse the teeth and mouth and gargle the throat well, morning and evening, with a few drops of Condy's ozonised water, in plain water. After each meal take a powder containing 10 grs. powdered vegetable charcoal and 5 grs. of bicarbonate of soda.

Bronchitis

The following prescription is recommended: Carbonate of ammonia 35grs., ipecacuanha wine 2 drs., spirit of choroform 1 dr. (1 to 7), paregoric 2 drs., water ad 8 oz. Mix and take one tablespoonful three times a day, or oftener if the cough is troublesome.

Bilious

Before going to bed take a gill of hot water and the juice of a lemon.

Blackheads

Wash with good soap several times a day. Afterwards rinse the soap off and dry with a rough, coarse towel. Take plenty of exercise and avoid rich food.

Blushing

Take half a wine-glassful of compound infusion of gentian twice a day.

Bunions

Shoe pressure must be avoided.

Paint them every second day with iodine till the soreness disappears.

Alternatively, belladonna and glycerine can be painted on.

Camphor Inhalations

Pour half-a-pint of boiling-hot water over a drachm of pulverised camphor, and inhale the vapours for 10 to 20 minutes. This gives great relief for a cold.

Carbuncle

Treatment must be both constitutional and local. Strength must be kept up by giving raw eggs, cream, milk, beef-tea, mutton-chops.

Alcohol should be given with the food, but over-stimulation must be guarded against. The bowels must be kept open.

Painting the surface with tincture of iodine three times a day hastens the formation of the openings in the skin, but if the pain is severe, painting with belladonna and glycerine, and hot compresses of dry wool, give more relief.

Hot fomentations are best avoided, as they encourage the formation of boils. When the openings form, a wet dressing of boracic lint the exact size of the swelling may be applied, covered with cotton wool and changed frequently.

When the discharge has diminished, the salicylic ointment dressing may be used.

Castor Oil

The best method for taking it is to float it on milk and, before taking, eat a piece of orange or lemon peel.

Catarrh

Take 25 parts roasted coffee, 1 part menthol, 25 parts of sugar, grind them together to a fine powder, and use as snuff. Glykaline is also beneficial.

Chapped Hands

Take the fat of mutton, melt and strain, and pour it into a basin to harden. Before it is hard, work it into a ball. To apply it, first hold before a fire until the surface is soft, then rub this soft tallow on the chaps, working it gently into the skin.

Or, mix a $\frac{1}{4}$ lb. of unsalted hog's lard, which has been washed in spring water and then rosewater, with the yolks of 2 new-laid eggs and a large spoonful of honey. Add as much fine oatmeal or almond-paste as will work into a paste.

Always dry the hands thoroughly after washing.

You can alternatively rub in boracic ointment or simple lanoline. Glycerine is effective in some cases, but causes much smarting.

Chapped Lips

Put a $\frac{1}{4}$-oz. of gum-benjamin, storax and spermaceti, some Alkanet-root, a chopped apple, bunch of bruised black grapes, a $\frac{1}{4}$-lb. unsalted butter and 2 oz. of beeswax into a new tin saucepan. Simmer gently till the wax, etc., is dissolved, then strain through a linen cloth. When cold, melt again, and pour into small pots or boxes; or, if to make cakes, use the bottoms of teacups.

Charcoal Powders

This often arrests putrid sores. It is placed above the dressings, and, not infrequently, quilted loosely in a little cotton wool.

Chilblains on Hands

In France, to treat this condition they take a piece of alum about the size of a nut, and melt it in enough hot water to cover the hands. When the alum is melted, soak your hands in the liquid for nearly a quarter-of-an-hour, then cover your hands at once with gloves, which you keep on all night, and as long as you can manage to do so during the day.

Chilblains

If they are broken, mix 2 fluid ounces of tincture of catechu, one ounce of honey, and 7 oz. of water, and treat them with this mixture.

You should do some active exercise, such as skipping, for a few minutes before going to bed and directly they are dressed in the morning.

Chilblain Liniment

Mix together 2 oz. of methylated chloroform, 8 grains of cocaine hydrochlorate, 3 oz. of compound camphor liniment, 5 oz. of liniment of soap, colour with cochineal, and filter.

Chilblain Ointment

Take 20 minims of oil of lavender, 10 minims liquid carbolic acid, and 1 oz. of oxide of zinc ointment, mix together to make an ointment, and apply at night.

For broken chilblains, take black oxide of iron bole and oil of turpentine, each 1 dr., rub together and add mixture to 1 oz. melted resin cerate.

A Russian remedy is to dry the peel of cucumbers and, when required, soften the inner part with water and apply to the affected part.

Colds

In the earliest stages, such old-fashioned, time-honoured remedies as a hot mustard foot-bath, hot sleeping draughts, or the like, taken to provoke abundant sweating, are excellent, but must be taken at the outset to do good.

An old piece of cold-prevention advice called for habitual, persistent attention to the following rules:

"Walk with the toes turned outward. Walk with the chin slightly above the horizontal line, as if looking at the top of a man's hat in front of you, or at the eaves or roof of a house. Walk a good deal with your hands behind you. Sit with the lower part of your spine pressed against the chair-back."

Keep handy an inhaler. Add 5 drops of eucalyptus oil to the water in the inhaler; inhale for 7 minutes, drawing the gas up through the mouth and letting it out through the nostrils, and afterwards through each nostril in turn.

Five drops of spirit of camphor, on sugar, will often prevent a cold if taken at once.

To relieve a chest cold, wring out a piece of flannel in boiling water, and sprinkle it with turpentine and lay it on the chest.

To cure a head cold, inhale constantly with chloride of ammonium in which 4 drops of oil of eucalyptus have been put.

There are many ways in which a cold may be arrested. A good dose of quinine, 6 to 10 grs., is an effective remedy. Bathe the feet in hot water and drink a pint of hot lemonade, after which sponge with hot water and stay in a warm room, and bathe the face constantly with hot water.

Snuff hot water up the nostrils every 3 hours.

Inhale ammonia or menthol.

Take 4 hours' active exercise in the open air.

More than a century ago, the web of the black spider was thought to cure ague. Cobwebs were a popular remedy for fever.

In some country districts, there are still many folk who believe that swallowing a spider will cure them. Pepper is also a popular remedy, and many take a teaspoonful of pepper in a glass of gin.

Grandmother knew a man who claimed to have cured himself of the 'flu by putting into his boots a half-gill of hot whisky and putting the boots instantly on. The very first day he tried it the fever came as usual, but there was no chill; the second day the symptoms were modified; and after the third application there was no return of fever.

He said: "I well remember, when a boy, there being a tavern in our neighbourhood where teamsters stopped to rest and water their horses, of seeing the carters instead of drinking their half-gill of whisky, pouring it into their boots cold, as a protection against the frost. They told me there was nothing equal to it to warm the feet; that it was better than fire, for the feet remained warm for a long time and prevented sickness. It is also excellent for a cold, or when from exposure, the feet got wet or damp, and a cold or other disease may be apprehended. I have known it to act like a charm."

When it comes to generally looking after health, many notable men have been convinced that habitual moderation in eating and drinking was essential to the full and healthy employment of their intellect. Sir Isaac Newton, when he applied himself to the investigation of light and colour, to quicken his faculties and enable him to fix his attention, confined himself all the time to a small quantity of bread, with a little sack-and-water. He took a little whenever he felt his strength flag.

Grandmother used to point out that some will wrap

the head on going to bed in a flannel nightcap, and take a glass of negus warm, whey, or gruel: another will take a tumbler of cold water with or without a spoonful of sal volatile. A very good way to stop catarrh on its accession is to go to bed early, to take a warm drink with a mild aperient pill, half-an-ounce Epsom salts, or a Seidlitz powder, early the following morning.

Generally, an abstemious diet should be observed, and drinks such as barley-water, freely taken. A mild aperient should be administered—a dose of compound senna mixture, followed by a dose of saline mixture, and at bed-time, 5 grains of Dover's powder taken and the legs bathed as high as the knees in warm water for 10 minutes. If the catarrh is severe, it is better to stay in bed, but not keep too warm, or be wrapped in too much clothing. This may accelerate cure of the cold, but will increase susceptibility to a recurrence of the attack.

A cold must be broken within the first 48 hours, or it will run its course. As soon as a person discovers he has a cold, he should stay in a room of uniform temperature, drink warm drinks, bathe his feet in hot water, and take 4 compound cathartic pills at bed-time, and a drachm of Epsom salts in the morning. He shouldn't eat meat for a few days, and if the chest is painful, apply a porous plaster.

*   *   *

Another school recommends abstinence from food, or not to eat anything except a piece of dry bread for breakfast and dinner, and nothing for supper; and liberal indulgence in cold water, drinking at least 2 tumblers on going to bed and on rising in the morning.

A cold can often be broken if the person, as soon as he gets the first symptoms, abstains from food for, say, 36 hours, goes to bed in a warm room, wraps up well, and drinks plenty of hot drinks.

The majority of colds are caught by cooling off too quickly after exercise. Persons exercise until perspiration is produced, then try to cool off.

Anyone exposed to cold or wet through the day should bathe his feet and hands in warm water at night, and they will escape many colds and serious illnesses.

An "old woman's bath" will do good, too. This is an old-fashioned "sweat" brought about by being tucked up in bed in warm blankets, and drinking hot teas until a most profuse perspiration is induced and kept up for hours. Even after you have run the risk of taking cold you can often escape by removing all damp clothes as quickly as possible, soaking the feet for 10 minutes in hot mustard-water, applying a large mustard plaster to the back and covering up well with warm blankets in a warm room to produce free perspiration. Perspiration is promoted by drinking one or two cups of hot tea—camomile tea, for example. Home remedies, promptly applied, can prevent serious illness.

For the cough attending a common cold the following is an excellent cough syrup: Take an ounce thoroughwort, an ounce of slippery elm, an ounce of stick liquorice, and one ounce of flax seed. Simmer together in a quart of water until the strength is entirely extracted. Strain carefully, add a pint of molasses and half-a-pound of loaf sugar. Simmer them together and, when cold, bottle tight.

Generally, it is better not to stop a cough—especially in children. A cough is Nature's way of bringing up phlegm which would otherwise accumulate.

Ipecacuanha wine will, by loosening the phlegm, loosen the cough, which is the right way to get rid of a cough.

Constipation

Finely chop 1 lb. of figs and 2 oz. of senna leaves; add a cupful of treacle; mix well and put into well-covered earthenware pots. Dosage for an adult, $\frac{1}{2}$ teaspoonful; for a child, $\frac{1}{4}$ teaspoonful.

For habitual constipation, obtain pills made of $4\frac{1}{2}$ grains of resin of podophyllin; the same of soap and of extract of hyoscyamus; divide into 10 pills. A grain-and-a-half of extract of rhubarb added to each pill makes them still more effective.

Corns

Most corn remedies contain potash or acetic acid, substances which soften the epidermis, combined with various resins and pitch. They are good but do not cure the trouble if bad shoes are worn. Soft corns can be helped by daily washings with soap and water, and occasional use of spirits of camphor to harden the skin. Also wear cotton wool saturated with oil or glycerine between the toes.

Or, apply fresh every morning the yeast of small beer spread on a rag.

After paring the corns close, apply bruised ivy-leaves daily. Within a fortnight, they will drop out.

Apply chalk, powdered and mixed with water. This is also a good remedy for warts.

Corns can be eased by soaking the feet in hot water in which oatmeal has been boiled. This also soothes dry and hot feet.

For a corn caustic, use 4 drs. of tincture of iodine, 12 grs. of iodide of iron, 4 drs. of chloride of antimony; mix, and apply with a camelhair brush after paring the corn. Three applications should do the trick.

Yet another corn cure is effected by soaking a piece of bread in strong vinegar and applying as a poultice to the corn; the corn gets softened and can then be easily removed.

Or, soak the leaf of the common ground ivy overnight in strong vinegar, and keep it on the corn with the stocking. After wearing all day a fresh-soaked leaf should be used.

For especially persistent corns mix 1 dr. salicylic acid, 2 drops lactic acid, and 1 oz. of flexile collodion. Apply daily and you will soon be able to get the corns out. Soak the feet occasionally in water in which salt has been dissolved. Dry the feet carefully then powder them.

Alternatively, you should bathe the feet in lukewarm water for quarter-of-an-hour; take a razor blade and pare away the upper part of the corn. Then apply a mixture of 2 parts salicylic acid, 4 parts flexile collodian, 1 part creosote, and allow to dry.

Coughs

Make a hole through a lemon and fill it with honey. Roast it and catch the juice. Take a teaspoonful frequently.

Or, try ½-teaspoonful grated fresh horseradish, 2 teaspoonsful of honey. Take a dessertspoonful of this mixture at a time.

Or, cut a hole through the middle of a swede and fill the hole with brown sugar. Leave overnight, then drink the juice.

Or, take a teaspoonful every 3 hours of a mixture made with 1 teaspoonful castor oil, 1 teaspoonful glycerin, 1 teaspoonful lemon-juice.

An ancient remedy for coughing is to boil 2 or 3 snails in barley-water, but don't tell the patient.

Nervous coughing can be stopped by pressing on the nerves of the lip in the neighbourhood of the nose. Pressure there can prevent a cough at the outset. Sneezing can be stopped the same way. Pressing hard on the roof of the mouth can also stop coughing. Willpower can do wonders, too. There was a doctor who used to say, whenever he entered hospital wards: "The first patient who coughs will be deprived of food today." Patients rarely coughed then.

Effective relief can also be obtained by surrounding the neck with an envelope of wetted linen or cotton, oil-silk, and thick flannel in the order mentioned. This, too, is good for the croupy cough and breathing with which children are often attacked at night. As there is always dryness of the throat, water should also be given. A tea-spoonful of salt in a tumbler of water is a good gargle. Ordinary coughs seldom require more than frequent sipping of linseed tea. For bad chest coughs, application of a fomentation, prepared like the envelope of linen, oil-silk, and flannel for the throat, is best.

Cough Emulsion

Take 2 drachms gum ammoniac and half-a-pint water. Rub the ammoniac well, gradually adding the water, until well mixed, then strain through linen. This emulsion is good for coughs and asthma if no inflammatory symptoms are present. Dose is from 1 to 2 tablespoonsful taken with an equal quantity of almond emulsion.

Emulsions soothe irritation in the lungs, or alimentary canal, and are vehicles for substances that couldn't otherwise be so conveniently taken in liquid form.

Another useful cough mixture is made with 5 oz. honey, $\frac{1}{4}$-lb. treacle, 7 oz. vinegar. Mix and simmer for 15 minutes. When warm, add 2 drachms of ipecacuanha wine. Dose a tablespoonful every 4 hours for adults.

A purge at the outset of a cough can help. Also, a low diet, avoidance of exposure to cold, hot drinks of lemonade or elder-bloom tea, stimulating foot-baths—anything to secure free perspiration, and the relief of congestion by the inhalation of steam.

Coughs respond particularly well to water treatment. Night and morning wash feet and legs up to the knees in cold water, then rub very briskly with a rough towel until the skin glows. You should also frequently sniff tepid water up the nostrils and sip a tumblerful of hot water before each meal and just before retiring. This treatment can break a cold at the onset and prevent bronchitis developing.

Cough Lozenges

A very effective prescription uses 25 grs. ipecacuanha,

50 grs. Kermes mineral, 8 grs. codeine phosphate, 1½ oz. white sugar, 1½ oz. gum arabic, 1½ oz. extract of liquorice, 20 drops oil of aniseed, and some syrup of tolu to work into the mass. Form, roll, and cut into 160 lozenges. Take one three times a day.

Cough Mixture

Take some liquorice sticks, ½-pint flaxseed, and the rind of a lemon; put into a quart of water and allow to simmer for two days. Then add the juice of a lemon and ½-lb. brown sugar. Boil for 3 hours and strain. Add, when cool, ½-pint rum. Shake well and take a wine-glassful every morning fasting.

Or, mix 3 drs. pure terebene, 2 drs. ol. eucalypt. globul, 2 drs. syrup of tolu, and 2 oz. listerine. Shake the bottle and take a tablespoonful every 2 or 3 hours.

Croup

At the first croupy sound, wrap the child warmly and put its feet in mustard-water as warm as can be borne. At the same time give small doses, from 15 to 30 drops (according to age), of syrup of ipecac, repeating half-hourly till free vomiting takes place. Bathe neck and chest with camphorated oil, and keep warm with layers of flannel. After vomiting, a teaspoonful of a cough mixture (less for an infant), should be given every 3 or 4 hours until symptoms disappear. The cough mixture is simply a mixture of equal parts of sweet oil, paregoric, and syrup of ipecac. Equal parts of goose oil and honey rubbed on the throat and chest is first-rate if the patient is kept well covered and out of draughts. Alternatively, give a teaspoonful of ipecacuanha wine. If vomiting doesn't soon follow, give half the dose again. Keep the patient in bed. Warm a brick and when hot put it into a bucket of water placed at the bedside. This will cause warm vapour to rise and will help the patient breathe. Apply a warm poultice to the throat and use warm fomentations. Milk is the best diet. If this doesn't relieve, send for the doctor.

Some cases of pleurisy can be stopped if the patient, at the beginning of an attack, takes an alcohol or vapour bath to perspire freely, drinks plenty of strong tea made with catnip, and keeps well covered in bed.
(Casual treatment for this is now considered dangerous. —Editor.)

Turpentine may be applied over the seat of the pain and mustard on the feet. Rubbing the arms and legs with dry flannel helps to moderate the severity of the attack. Call a doctor if relief isn't obtained in a few hours.

Dandruff

Take an ounce of sulphur and a quart of water; shake constantly every few hours and saturate the head every morning with the liquid. Dandruff will disappear in a week or so, and the hair become bright and glossy.

Or, you can wash the head with coaltar soap, and sponge with boracic lotion. A weak sulphur and lanoline ointment can be used.

Dry Lips

When lips, gums and tongue are dry and coated with mucus in acute illness, they should be washed several times daily with glycerine diluted with an equal quantity of water. A little lemon-juice or a few drops of rosewater can be added to make it pleasanter.

Dysentery

Use an enema of an ounce of starch gruel in which you have put 2 grs. of iodoform.

Ear-ache

Wet a bit of cotton wool in corn oil; gather into it a pinch of black pepper, and insert in the ear.

Ear Wax

At bedtime, put a few drops of olive oil into each ear, then close with a piece of cotton wool. A doctor or nurse will clear the loosened wax with a proper syringe.

Eyes

Bathing the eyes several times a day in cold water makes them bright.

* * *

If you have any discoloration around the eyes, get the fresh root of Solomon's seal, scrape it like horseradish, moisten with vinegar, and apply to the injury.

* * *

For a stye in the eye, bathe frequently with warm milk and water, or in warm poppy water if very painful. When the stye bursts, smear along the edge of the eyelid with one part of citrine ointment and four parts of spermaceti, well mixed.

* * *

Hot boracic fomentations can help burst the stye.

* * *

If an eyelash is seen situated in the centre of a stye it should be pulled out. Give quinine and iron tonics to improve your general resistance.

* * *

To treat weak eyes, play a jet of weak salt water (a teaspoonful of salt to a half-pint of water) on the eyelid. This is a strengthener. Bathing the eyes with cold water before washing preserves and keeps them strong.

Feet

People suffering with cold feet should put them into hot

water for 10 minutes before going to bed, then plunge them into cold water for a second; wipe dry and rub till warm. Put on a pair of cotton socks wrung out of cold or tepid water, draw over them a pair of thick lamb's wool stockings, and sleep in them.

For perspiring feet, dip them in cold water a minute every morning and sprinkle pulverised tannin at the bottom of the shoes every other day. Wash the feet in warm water nightly, after which, dip them into cold water a moment.

Or, a foot-bath of salt and water is first-rate for perspiring feet. Or, dust the feet every night for a week, and afterwards once a week, with the following application: Mix 2 parts salicylic acid and 3 parts burnt alum. If the perspiration causes the feet to be unpleasant, an application of subnitrate of bismuth should be rubbed over them.

Alternatively, wash the feet every night with water containing a little ammonia, and rub them with ammonia, especially between the toes. Woollen stockings should be worn and the feet powdered with perfumed talcum powder.

For swollen, sore, or blistered feet, use 3 parts of salicylic acid, 10 parts of starch, and 87 parts of finely pulverised soapstone, and dust into shoes and stockings.

For tired feet, immerse them for 10 minutes in 2 quarts of cold water, 2 tablespoonsful of ammonia and 1 tablespoonful of bay rum. Bathe the water over the limbs to the knees, then rub dry with a towel. The tired feeling will go.

Fomentations

Flannel, spongio-piline, or "gamgee-tissue," should be wrung out in boiling water as follows:

The material should be wrapped in a towel folded lengthwise and placed in a basin with the ends of the towel hanging over the edge. Pour boiling water into the basin, and seize the ends of the towel and twist in reverse ways to wring out the water. Untwist the towel and the fomentation—be sure it is not too hot—should then be placed on the part, covered with oiled silk, then a layer of cotton wool, and secured with flannel bandage.

Headache

For many types of headache, a towel wrung out of water as hot as can be borne and wound round the head gives relief.

Or, take a wide-mouthed, glass-stoppered bottle; half fill with fine sponge, and pour on 3 drs. of a solution of bisulphide of carbon. Apply the mouth of the bottle to the temple or as near as possible to the seat of pain, close so that none of the vapour can escape, and keep it there 5 minutes or so.

After a minute or two, tingling is felt, which in 3 or 4 minutes increases. It subsides if the bottle is removed, as will any redness of the skin. This is especially good for neuralgia and nervous headaches.

A saline wash for headaches is made by mixing a half-ounce of salt, 4 fluid ounces each of vinegar and soft water, 2 fluid ounces of brandy. Be sure the salt is fully dissolved. This is an effective cooling wash for headaches and can also sometimes be used tepid.

Heartburn

Take 2 tablespoonsful 3 times a day between meals of a mixture made with 3 drs. sulphite of soda, 3 drs. sal volatile, 2 drs. of tincture of ginger, 8 oz. infusion of quassia. Take a tablespoonful of whisky in warm water with your meals.

Or, immediately after meals, take a teaspoonful of

G

wheat charcoal plus a tablespoonful of glycerin just before or after meals.

Housemaid's Knee

Is due to prolonged kneeling and inflammation of the bursa over the ligament of the knee-cap. The elbow, buttock, and back of the knees are also sometimes affected, especially in rheumatic and gouty persons.

Use soft pads to kneel on. When inflamed, the joint must be rested and cold applied. After acute symptoms, or in cases of slow formation, paint with iodine and apply pressure with strapping or a bandage, and avoid further irritation.

Indigestion

A quarter-of-an-hour before meals, take 2 tablespoonsful of a mixture made of $1\frac{1}{2}$ dr. of carbonate of bismuth, $1\frac{1}{3}$ dr. of carbonate of magnesia, $1\frac{1}{2}$ oz. of mucilage of tragacanth, and 8 oz. of water. Or, drink a teacupful of very hot water when going to sleep; in the morning half-a-cupful of milk filled up with boiling water, and eat whole wheatmeal bread.

If you have severe stomach pain through indigestion, drink the juice of half a large lemon, or sweet orange, every day immediately after dinner.

Influenza

Go to bed in a warm, well-ventilated room. Diet should consist of soda and milk, alternated with beef-tea or broths. Old people require stimulants, best given in the form of brandy, egg, and milk mixture. Give plenty of fluid. During the profuse perspirations a flannel night-dress, frequently changed, should be worn.

Ingrowing Nails

Rarely occur if nails are properly attended. Toe nails

should never be cut too short, and always square across, with corners carefully preserved and not rounded. Skin debris, forming a soft pad under the nail, should never be picked out with a knife or scissors.

The foot should be soaked in hot water. Thin the nail by scraping. If very painful, apply a linseed poultice. When irritation has subsided, cotton wool should be pressed between the flesh and the nail, and after, saturate it with iodine: do this for several days. If it is necessary to raise the end of the nail, press cotton wool between it and the toe.

Liver

If your liver is sluggish, drink a glass of hot water with the juice of half-a-lemon squeezed into it, night and morning, without any sugar.

Lumbago

For lumbago or sprains, mix a beaten raw egg with ½-pint of vinegar, an ounce of spirits of turpentine, ¼-oz. of spirits of wine, and the same of camphor. Beat together, bottle, and shake for 10 minutes. It must be tightly corked. In half-an-hour it will be ready. Rub in well 3 or 4 times daily after warming the affected part with a hot-water bottle or in front of a fire.

For similar pains and rheumatic conditions, mix 2 oz. of mustard with ½-pint of spirits of wine and 2 drs. of camphor. Let the mixture stand 2 or 3 days, corked in a bottle. Strain off and keep closely bottled for use.

Mustard Plaster

To make a soothing mustard plaster, mix mustard with the white of an egg instead of water. This plaster will draw without blistering.

Mustard Poultice

Should be made the same way as linseed, except by adding a tablespoonful of mustard to the linseed. It can also be made of the mustard powder alone, or in combination with bread crumbs or linseed meal. When only mustard is used, the powder should be moistened with water and the paste produced spread on a piece of linen and covered with muslin as a protective between the mustard and the skin. When mixed with linseed, the powder and the meal may be incorporated before water is added, or the meal may be moistened and spread on linen for application and the mustard then spread on the surface. Mustard leaves can be used in the place of mustard poultices, only require wetting before application, and are both clean and economical.

Another recipe requires the poultice, made in the usual way. Dip a sponge into it, wrap it in a soft handkerchief, and apply to the part. By warming the sponge again and moistening it afresh, it can be re-applied and the strength is preserved.

Nails

To whiten nails, mix 2 drs. of diluted sulphuric acid, 1 dr. tincture of myrrh, and 4 oz. filtered water. Cleanse the hands with soap and then dip the fingers into this mixture.

Nausea

A cup of hot water before meals will prevent nausea.

Milk

To increase mother's milk, drink a pint of water going to bed, or drink largely of soup made with lentils.

Neuralgia

An excellent liniment for neuralgia is made by mixing a

pint of methylated spirits, 2 oz. each of cedar bark, sassafras, and origanum, 1 oz. of powdered carbonate of ammonia.

Mix well and apply with lint to the gums round the teeth, or to the face in neuralgic pain, by wetting brown paper and laying on the parts. Never too long for fear of blistering.

This is also good for rheumatic pains.

Another remedy is made by mixing 1 part of iodoform to 10 to 15 of collodion. Spread thinly and repeatedly on the neuralgic surface, it is usually effective. If not, the application should be repeated.

Onions

If your breath smells strongly after onion eating, a cup of strong coffee will remove all smell of onions from the breath.

Perspiration

People who perspire a lot should use a teaspoonful of cloudy ammonia in the bath. Some alum, borax, or ammonia in the water is very good, then powder the most affected parts with talcum or rice powder.

Or, melt as much boracic acid as half-a-pint of water will dissolve, and apply to the parts which perspire, and keep well powdered with talcum. When perspiration under the arms stains clothing, put thick pads of cotton wool over dress preservers near the skin, bathe with Eau de Cologne and water, and rub plenty of talcum powder well in.

Eau de Cologne dabbed under the arms after washing or bathing helps to close the pores and to reduce profuse perspiration.

Piles

Eat a large boiled leek.

Rheumatism

Salicylate of soda. Start with 5 grs. in a wineglass of water, and increase the dose to 20 grs. This is not for those with weak hearts.

A lotion for rheumatism is made with a tablespoonful of cayenne, 4 tablespoonsful of salt. Pour on a pint of boiling vinegar. When cold, take 2 oz. of tincture of myrrh and 1 dr. of essential oil of spearmint, sassafras and origanum; shake the oils well together with the tincture of myrrh before mixing with the vinegar, cayenne and salt. Bathe the parts affected, or rub gently. Take 2 pills 3 times a day made of 1 oz. powdered poke root, the same of gum guaiacum, ½ oz. of lobelia.

Rheumatism: Pine Baths

Excellent for gout and rheumatism. Prepare by emptying a bottle of pinol extract into an ordinary bath for adults, and half-a-bottle for children. Pinol is good as a deodoriser in sick rooms.

Ringworm

Shake ½ dr. red iodide of mercury; 1 dr. iodide of sodium, and 3 drs. of water in a bottle till dissolved. Cork and keep ready for use. When required, take a spoonful and add to it 3 of water. Mix well and apply to the parts with a camel-hair brush. Do not repeat for several days.

Ringworm can also be cured in 10 days by cutting the hair off the affected spot; rubbing in turpentine and washing off with carbolic soap. Then wash the whole head with hot water and touch the spots with diluted iodine, repeating once or twice a day.

Rough Skin

Use tepid filtered water with lanoline soap. This should

be applied with rubber gloves. Very soft towels are necessary for drying the skin gently. The roughness should then be treated with a little cold cream. Rub into the skin every night some borax ointment. A little Hunyadi water taken occasionally and a dose of Bourbole water twice a day after food is beneficial.

Sleeplessness

Warm, easily-digested food is the most valuable of all sleeping draughts. Mental work should always be stopped half-an-hour before retiring and some relaxation indulged in, such as a short walk, exercise, or a not too exciting book. A sedentary life and intense mental work should be countered by periods of active exercise. Over-fatigue is best treated by a tepid bath or sponging, and a long draught of water before going to bed. A teaspoonful of salt in a pint of hot water is also useful.

When sleeplessness is due to worry, try to divert the thoughts by taking deep breaths and breathing out gently and slowly through the nostrils and fixing attention on the outflowing stream of air; counting sheep; repeating a nursery rhyme over and over; watching, in imagination, a sailing ship.

Drugs should never be taken except under medical advice.

Sleep will do much to cure irritability. It restores vigour to an over-worked brain. It builds and strengthens a weak body. It cures headache. Sleep is Nature's greatest cure-all.

A remedy for insomnia suited to almost everybody is eating onions. Common raw onions should be taken, but Spanish onions, stewed, will do. This is due to a peculiar essential oil in onions. This oil has great soporific powers. Eat 2 or 3 onions, and the effect is magical.

Take onion soup or syrup of onions every night. Onion jelly is also very soothing. To make it, shred 2 or 3 good-sized onions in a little stock and stew till tender. Add a squeeze of fresh lemon to make the onions digestible for the most delicate stomach, then pour in enough hot water for the quantity and thickness of the soup. Boil ten minutes. Season and add a small piece of butter.

When awakened and unable to sleep easily again, get out of bed, beat and turn your pillow, shake the bedclothes well, then throw the bed open and leave it to cool. Meanwhile, walk about awhile, then return to bed. You will soon fall asleep.

If you don't want to get out of bed, lift up your bedclothes, draw in fresh air, and let them fall, forcing it out again. Repeat 20 times.

Old people examined to assess the causes of their longevity agreed on one thing—all went to bed early and rose early.

> Early to bed, and early to rise,
> Makes a man healthy, wealthy, and wise.

Snoring

Sometimes due to thickening and partial stoppage of the nostrils. In such cases little can be done. Smoking may cause it; sometimes it is because the stomach is out of order, and a mild laxative should be taken. Heavy dinners, too many bedclothes, and unventilated rooms, can all cause snoring.

Stiffness

A remedy for stiffness after exertion is a good soaking for 10 minutes in a bath of the hottest water that can be borne. Follow with vigorous rubbing all over with coarse, hot towels. Afterwards rub a little camphorated oil into the skin and knead all the muscles thoroughly with the hands for 15 minutes. Then take 10 grs. of salicylate of soda in a wine-glassful of water at bedtime, and enjoy a brisk walk next morning.

Tapeworm

A draught containing bitter aloes should be taken in the morning. The evening before, take a laxative saline draught. This works every time.

Throat Soreness

Mix $\frac{1}{4}$-oz. finely pulverised sulphur with 3 oz. of pure honey. Dilute with vinegar and use as a gargle.

Make a quart of red pepper tea, strain and add a tablespoonful of salt. Sweeten with honey. Gargle often with this lukewarm.

Get 2 large lemons, put in the oven until warm, peel and squeeze out the juice. Add $\frac{1}{4}$ lb. of best honey, mix well and add 2 dessertspoonsful of best glycerine. Mix well and bottle. Take a teaspoonful as often as necessary.

Throat Ulceration

Mix an ounce of powdered alum with the whites of 4 eggs and 2 oz. tincture of camphor. Use night and morning.

Toothache

Mix 60 drops of creosote or spirits of tar, 60 drops of brandy, 120 drops of sweet spirits of nitre. A piece of lint dipped into this and applied to the tooth can effect a cure.

Another toothache relief mixture is made by mixing 1 part bryonia liniment in 10 parts of warm water. Put a teaspoonful in half a wine-glassful of warm water and hold in the mouth over the aching tooth.

Voice

To strengthen the voice, take 2 drs. beeswax, 3 drs. balsam, 4 drs. powdered liquorice root. Melt the balsam with the wax in an earthen jar; when melted, remove from the stove, and while in a melted state, mix in the powder. Make pills of 3 grs. each and take 2 occasionally 3 or 4 times a day.

Whooping Cough

To allay paroxysms, try the following remedy:

Carbolic acid ⎱ each	7½ drops
Alcohol ⎰	
Tincture of iodine	5 drops
Peppermint water	750 drops
Tincture of belladonna	15 drops
Syrup of diacodium	150 drops

A tablespoonful should be given every 2 hours till paroxysms stop.

A valuable remedy for whooping cough is to get a long-spouted kettle to spread steam into the room. Fill the kettle to the spout-hole. When the water boils put in a tablespoonful of carbolic acid, then let the steam from the kettle fill the room. This relieves.

Whooping cough can be helped if the child takes, morning, noon and night for four days, a dose of finely-ground alum mixed in a small quantity of powdered sugar.

The dose varies from 1 to 2 grains according to the age of the child. If necessary, after the fourth day a child 8 years old must take 7 grains of ground alum 3 times a day. Milk diet is forbidden, and cold air avoided.

To relieve whooping cough, you can obtain a preparation called "Crysolyne" made from tar. Place a little in a saucer and put a nightlight under it. The "Crysolyne" will evaporate but it must not be left to burn. The fumes will relieve the cough and produce sleep.

Or, take 1 pint strongest West Indian rum, 2 oz. anise oil, 1 pint honey and 4 oz. lemon-juice.

To ease soreness in the chest, rub with the following: Half-an-ounce oil of amber; half-an-ounce oil of cloves; an ounce of olive oil; two teaspoonsful of laudanum. Diet should consist principally of barley-water and whey.

God cures: the doctor gets the credit

It is easy for a man in health to preach patience to the sick

Causing a symptom to disappear is very seldom the cure of any human infirmity. The true course is to prevent the symptom

Sickness is a sort of old age; it teaches us a difference in our earthly state, and inspires us with thoughts of a future, better than a thousand volumes of philosophers and divines

The wise for cure on exercise depend, God never made His work for man to mend

Fond of lawsuits, little wealth Fond of doctors, little health

Who goes to bed supperless, all night tumbles and tosses

8

Grannie's
Cosmetics

RANNIE was not only a competent healer. She was, in her lighter moments, something of a beauty specialist, and her home-made lotions, balms and salves enjoyed a high reputation among the young women of the village and surrounding farms. Here are some of her favourites:

Complexion Cream

Take 1 oz. oil of sweet almonds; ½-dr. each of white wax and spermaceti, with a little balm. Melt in a glazed jar and pour into a mortar.Stir until it becomes smooth and cold. Add gradually 1 oz. of rose or orange flower water. Stir until well mixed and creamy. This makes the skin supple and smooth.

Complexion Hints

Cucumbers cut in slices and soaked in rum are great

complexion-improvers. Or, pare and cut small cucumbers and bring to the boil in water, then allow to cool. Strain and bottle for use.

Oatmeal made into a poultice, strained, and the liquid mixed with bay rum, is a great softener and whitener.

Boiling milk poured over violets is said to keep the skin white, soft, and free from wrinkles.

Freckles

Use an ounce of fresh cream; 8oz. milk; lemon-juice. brandy, and an ounce of Eau de Cologne, sugar, 1 dr. Boil and skim.

Another way is to apply 4 times daily a lotion made of ½ dr. of muriate of ammonia, 2 drs. of lavender water, and ½ pint of distilled water.

To make a freckle paste, take a teacupful of sour milk; scrape into it a quantity of horse radish; let it stand for several hours; strain well, and apply with a camel-hair brush 2 or 3 times daily.

The following recipes are also said to remove either freckles, tan, or sunburn, and are harmless.

Dip a bunch of green grapes in a basin of water; sprinkle with powdered alum and salt mixed; wrap the grapes in paper and bake them; then squeeze out the juice. Wash face with the liquid, which will usually remove either freckles, tan or sunburn.

Or, put 2 spoonsful of sweet cream into half-a-pint of milk. Squeeze in the juice of a lemon, add half-a-glass of brandy, a little alum and sugar; boil the whole, skim well, and when cool, it is ready for use.

Glycerin and lemon juice removes tan and subdues freckles, and freckles can be made dim by rubbing them daily with water in which a tablespoonful of powdered alum has been dissolved. Use a large glass.

Hair

Take 1 oz. of palma christi oil and perfume with some bergamot or lavender, and brush it well into the hair wherever it is getting thin.

Hair Tonic

Glycerin	4 oz.
Alcohol	2 oz.
Water of ammonia	2 oz.
Tincture of cantharides	2 dr.
Rosewater	4 oz.
Water	4 oz.

Don't use any other pomade or wash with this.

Hair Falling

Wet the head occasionally in salt and water. This is often most effective when hair is falling out.

When hair falling results after illness, frequent application of sage tea is first-class. Sponge the hair with it.

Hair Lotion

To strengthen the roots, simmer dock roots in water and rub in the strained liquid daily on the head.

For a good stimulating lotion take 10 gr. of sulphate of quinine, 1 oz. bay rum, $\frac{1}{2}$ oz. glycerine, 2 drs. tincture of cantharides, and 6 oz. of rosewater. Mix well and shake before using. Brush it gently into the scalp every morning.

A cleansing and restorative hair wash is made with the froth of a hard soap beaten with the yolk of an egg and a dessert spoonful of spirits of rosemary.

Hair Restorer

Make a wash of 45 gr. of sulphur, 20 gr. of acetate of lead, ½ oz. of glycerin, and 10 oz. of water well mixed.

An ointment for thin hair partings is made by mixing 2 drs. of balsam of tolu, 20 minims of oil of rosemary, 1 dr. of tincture of cantharides, ½ oz .castor oil, and 1½ oz. of prepared lard. Rub into the thin spots every night.

Superfluous Hairs

A solution of common soda occasionally applied to the upper lip withers hair. The best method of applying is to place a tooth-comb on the upper lip so that the hairs can pass through it, then brush over with the dissolved soda. When the alkali has had time to act the comb should be removed and the lip sponged. Smear with pomatum or glycerine to prevent redness. Don't apply too often or you may irritate the skin. A strong solution of potash can also be used similarly. Get some peroxide of hydrogen and apply to superfluous hairs with a small camel-hair brush; or rub petrol jelly over them, then rub gently at night with a piece of pumice-stone. Rinse afterwards with warm water.

Stains

For hand stains, clean with salt and lemon juice rubbed over the stains until they disappear. Wash with clean water; but the best thing to use is the little india-rubber brush and pumice-stone soap. Silver or sea sand soap and very warm water, using a stiff nail brush, make hands white, but they must not be exposed to the air for several hours after. Linseed oil is good for rough hands.

Lime Cream for the Hair

Mix 1 drachm of oil of bergamot with 16 oz. of melted

marrow; beat well, add 8 oz. of lime water and 1 oz. of tincture of cantharides. Mix well and bottle.

Lip Salve

Take 8 oz. of sweet almond oil, 4 oz. prepared mutton suet, 1½ oz. of white wax, 2 oz. of spermaceti and 20 drops of otto of roses. Steep a little alkanet root in the oil and strain before using. Melt the suet, wax and spermaceti together, then add the oil and otto of roses.

Tanning

To prevent skin tanning, dissolve 2 drs. of chloride of ammonia in 1 pint of rose water, and 10 drops of otto of roses in 1 oz. of spirits of wine. Mix the two solutions and add 1 oz. of powdered Venetian talc. Sponge on the skin in the morning after bathing.

Tobacco

To remove tobacco odour from the breath, take 1 teaspoonful of tincture of myrrh, ½-teaspoonful of spirits of camphor, and add a pint of hot water in which some borax has been dissolved. Use a wine-glassful of this mixture to half-a-tumbler of water when brushing the teeth.

Tooth Powder

Two drs. Castile soap, ½-oz. powdered orris root, 2 drs. borax, 2 oz. precipitated chalk, 30 minims carbolic acid, 40 minims oil of eucalyptus. Mix well and brush the teeth with it, using tepid water.

To remove blackness from teeth, mix 1 oz. of muriatic acid, 1 oz. of water, and 2 oz. of honey. Wet a brush freely with the preparation and briskly rub the teeth. Immediately wash out the mouth with water to prevent the acid affecting the teeth enamel. Only use when the teeth are stained again.

Wrinkles

To remove wrinkles, mix 2 oz. juice of lily bulbs, 2 oz. Narboone honey, 1 oz. white wax, 3 drs. rosewater. Melt the wax with gentle heat and add the other ingredients. Apply at night and don't wipe off until morning.

Or, smooth the wrinkles by rubbing olive oil into them every night before going to bed.

A good life
keeps off wrinkles

A blithe heart makes a blooming visage

*'Tis good to walk till the blood appears on the cheek,
but not the sweat on the brow*

*They who would be young when they are old, must be
old when they are young*

*Few believe how far a little health, well managed, may
be made to go*

*The loss of our strength is much oftener occasioned by
the vices of our youth than by the ravages of age; it is
early intemperance and licentiousness that consign to
old age a worn-out constitution*

*Here is a short prescription for a healthful and happy
old age: Short but cheerful meals, music, and a good
conscience*

The Healing
Herb

The herbs which Grannie used in her remedies and recipes—and a great number of others, too—are available today. For the reader's interest and information, here is a list of Herb Simples obtainable from good herbalists. We are grateful to the well-known firm of Heath and Heather Ltd., of St. Albans, for having kindly checked the list

Herb Simples

AGRIMONY: For coughs, simple diarrhoea, relaxed bowels.

ANGELICA: For kidneys and to induce perspiration.

ASH LEAVES: For gouty, arthritic and rheumatic conditions.

AVENS: For diarrhoea.

BALM: Cooling for fevers; to induce mild perspiration.

BLACKBERRY: An excellent tonic; useful in cases of diarrhoea, etc.

BLADDERWRACK: For kidneys, and in bath for rheumatic conditions.

BLUE MALLOW: For coughs and colds.

BORAGE: For chest and fevers.

BROOM: For bladder complaints.

BUCHU: For urinary affections, gravel, inflammation of the bladder.

BUCKBEAN: For liver troubles, some skin diseases, rheumatism.

BUGLOSS: For fevers and inflammatory pains.

BURDOCK: For blood purifying. Seeds used for kidney affections.

BURNET (*Greater*): Useful for bleeding piles.

BURR MARIGOLD: Used in gouty and kidney complaints.

CALAMINT: For coughs, bronchitis, etc.

CARROT, WILD: For coughs, bronchitis, etc.

CELANDINE: For jaundice.

CENTURY: For dyspepsia; with other herbs for jaundice.

CLIVERS: For gravel and other urinary disorders. Also as a tonic.

COLTSFOOT: For coughs and in herbal smoking mixtures.

COMFREY: For chest troubles, for reducing inflammatory swelling; as poultice for healing superficial wounds.

CRANESBILL: For diarrhoea, incontinence of urine. Root to stop bleeding.

DAMIANA: For tonic in nervous and debilitated conditions.

DANDELION: With other herbs used for kidneys and liver. Also as a laxative and tonic. Roots as substitute for coffee.

FUMITORY: Used for stomach and liver derangements and for skin affections.

GERMANDER: Has been used for rheumatic and gouty affections; intermittent fevers.

GOLDEN ROD: For stomach weakness and to promote perspiration.

GROUND IVY: For indigestion and kidneys.

HEARTSEASE: For catarrh and for blood impurity. Also for skin eruptions in children.

HOREHOUND: For coughs, colds and chest complaints as a tonic, and for making Horehound Ale.

HORSETAIL: For gravel and for the kidneys.

HYSSOP: For coughs, colds and the chest.

IRISH MOSS: For chest and bronchial affections and for bladder and kidneys.

LADIES MANTLE: For excessive menstruation.

LILY OF THE VALLEY: Cardiac tonic.

LIVERWORT: For disorders of liver and kidneys.

LOOSESTRIFE: Used to check bleedings from nose, wounds, etc., and as a gargle for relaxed throat.

LUNGWORT: For coughs and chest.

MARJORAM, WILD: Used to promote perspiration and for internal chills.

MARSHMALLOW: For coughs and bronchitis and for bladder complaints. Root is used for reducing inflammation.

MEADOWSWEET: For kidneys and diarrhoea in children.

MISTLETOE: For nervous complaints and circulatory disorders.

MOTHERWORT: For nervous complaints and morning sickness, and as a mild tonic in convalescence.

MOUNTAIN FLAX: Useful for constipation and kidney complaints combined with other herbs.

MOUSEAR: For whooping cough and the chest.

MUGWORT: Used in combination with other herbs.

MULLEIN: For coughs and bronchitis.

NETTLES, STINGING: Very rich in chlorophyll, Used for nettle-rash, rheumatism and blood purifying. Also for making teetotal botanic beer.

PARSLEY PIERT: For gravel, kidney and bladder complaints.

PELLITORY OF THE WALL: For correcting suppression of urine and for gravel, etc.

PENNYROYAL: For spasms, flatulence and internal chills.

PEPPERMINT: Used to allay flatulence, stomach sickness and vomiting, and as a cordial.

PERIWINKLE: Astringent and tonic.

PILEWORT: Used for piles, internally as medicine, and externally in the form of ointment.

PLAINTAIN: For diarrhoea, piles and in blood medicines. Fresh leaves relieve insect bites.

RAGWORT: For coughs, colds, influenza, sciatica and rheumatism.

RASPBERRY: Chiefly used as an aid during pregnancy.

RED SAGE: As a gargle for a relaxed throat, laryngitis, quinsy and the tonsils. Also for ulcerated mouth and throat.

ROSEMARY: For headaches, nerves and stomach. As stimulant for the hair.

RUE: Used in small doses for hysteria.

RUPTUREWORT: Especially useful for catarrh of the bladder.

SANICLE: Used with other herbs for blood impurities, dysentery and diarrhoea.

SCABIOUS: Used with other herbs for coughs, fevers and internal inflammation.

SCULLCAP: For hysteria and nervous disorders.

SENNA LEAVES: Laxative. Usually prepared with a little ginger to modify griping effect.

SHEPHERD'S PURSE: For kidneys and diarrhoea.

SILVERWEED: Astringent and has tonic properties.

SOAPWORT: For skin complaints.

SOUTHERNWOOD: Used for worms in children.

SPEEDWELL: For colds, coughs. Also for skin troubles.

ST. JOHN'S WORT: For coughs, bronchitis and the lungs. Also for urinary complaints.

TANSY: For hysteria, morning sickness and for the kidneys. Also for the expulsion of worms in children.

THYME: For coughs, catarrh, sore throat and whooping cough.

UVA URSI: For gravel, kidneys and bladder complaints.

VERVAIN: For nervous disorders.

VIOLET: Antiseptic expectorant.

WOODRUFF: For liver and stomach complaints.

WOOD SAGE: For colds and fevers.

WORMWOOD: For strengthening the digestion; debility and for the expulsion of worms.

YARROW: For promoting perspiration for colds and fevers.

GRANNIES' REMEDIES

Barks

CHERRY: Used with other herbs for catarrhal affections.

POPLAR: Its valuable tonic properties are used in debility, indigestion, etc.

SLIPPERY ELM: Used for its most valuable healing and nutritive properties, as gruel or food, for stomach inflammation.

WILLOW, BLACK: Sedative, tonic.

Flowers

CHAMOMILE: Used in hysterical and nervous conditions, also as a digestive tonic and for debility.

CLOVER (RED): Used for bronchial coughs and whooping cough.

ELDER: A blood purifier; reduces fever and is used in urinary complaints.

HOPS: For sleeplessness and nerves. Also with other herbs for indigestion, debility and worms.

LIME: For headaches, soothing the nerves and for indigestion.

Seeds and Berries

ANISEED: Used in cough medicine and lozenges.

BURDOCK: One of the best blood purifiers. Often used with other herbs for this purpose.

CELERY: For rheumatism.

CORIANDER: Used with other herbs for flatulence. Also used for its flavouring qualities.

FENNEL: Used as a stomach medicine with other herbs.

JUNIPER: Used for kidneys, with other herbs.

LINSEED: Used in cough medicines and for poultices.

MUSTARD SEED: Emetic. Used as poultice for acute local pains in bronchitis, etc. The oil used in Mus-gar ointment.

NETTLE: Useful in chest affections and as a blood medicine.

SENNA PODS: Laxative. Usually taken with ginger to prevent griping.

Roots

BETH: Useful in cases of profuse menstruation.

BURDOCK ROOT: Used universally in herbal practice for blood purifying.

COMFREY ROOT: Used in chest complaints and as a poultice for healing superficial wounds.

COUCHGRASS: Used in bladder complaints, cystitis and for gout and rheumatism.

GRANNIES' REMEDIES

CRANESBILL ROOT: For infantile diarrhoea and incontinence of urine.

DANDELION ROOT: For kidneys and liver. An excellent coffee is made from the root when roasted and ground.

ECHINACEA: A blood purifier of great power. For boils, etc. Improves digestion.

ELECAMPANE: Used with other herbs for coughs and bronchitis.

GENTIAN: Taken before food it stimulates the appetite. It is a tonic in anaemia and dyspepsia.

GINGER: For colds and flatulence.

GOLDEN SEAL: For liver and disordered digestion, and for gastric trouble, dyspepsia and debility; also especially for catarrhal conditions of the mucous membranes. Used also as an eye lotion.

LIQUORICE: Much used for coughs and chest complaints.

MANDRAKE: Used to stimulate the glands to healthy action; for biliousness and liver disorders. Used in small doses at frequent intervals on account of its potency.

MARSHMALLOW: For relief of asthma, also dysentery and kidney troubles.

ORRIS: Of no remedial value. Used in tooth pastes, powders, etc., for fragrance.

SARSAPARILLA, JAMAICA: Used as blood purifier.

TORMENTIL: For diarrhoea, dysentery, etc. Good for sores and cuts.

Gum Resin

MYRHH: Used as tincture for inflammatory sore throat. Also as a gargle and mouth-wash, especially when ulceration is present.

Herb Simples

EYEBRIGHT: For weak eyes.

FIGWORT: Used for wounds. Applied as a poultice.

INDEX

GRANNIES' REMEDIES

GRANNIES' REMEDIES

GRANNIES' REMEDIES